Foundation Licence

The Foundation
Amateur Radio Licence
Students' Manual
5th Edition

by Alan Betts, G0HIQ

Published by the
Radio Society of Great Britain
www.rsgb.org
Tel: 01234 832 700 Fax: 01234 831 496

First published 2001 & Reprinted
2001, 2002, 2003, 2004, 2005 & 2006

5th edition first published in 2007
Reprinted ten times 2008 - 2016

ISBN 9781-8723-0980-4

Cover design:
Jodie Escott, M3TPQ

Design & Editing:
Steve White, G3ZVW

Cartoons:
Gary Milton, G0CUQ

Production & Revisions:
Mark Allgar, M1MPA

Printed in Great Britain by
Latimer Trend Ltd
of Plymouth

Any amendments or updates to this book can be found at www.rsgb.org/main/publications-archives/books-extra/

Publishers Note
The opinions expressed in this book are those of the author and not necessarily those of the RSGB. Whilst the information presented is believed to be correct, the publishers and their agents cannot accept responsibility for consequences arising from any inaccuracies or omissions.

Contents

Introduction

THE FOUNDATION Licence is intended to attract new people, young and the not-so-young into amateur radio and to simplify the procedure for getting your first licence.

So, welcome to amateur radio.

What is amateur radio?

WELL, IT'S A HOBBY, a technical hobby with a very large number of different activities within it. It might mean talking to your friends by radio - a bit like a mobile phone without the phone bill. It might mean talking to people half way round the world, with friends, or with someone who replied to a call.

You can link your radio to a computer and send text or pictures, very much like the Internet, but where you can have a lot more control over what happens and how your call is routed. You could learn how that control and routing is done, a skill that will be valuable if your career interests include the Internet or computer networking.

You may wish to learn Morse code, which will make long distance contacts easier and will overcome some of the difficulties if you do not have a common language. Morse transmitters and receivers are easy to make, so you could use a transmitter/receiver that you built yourself. Perhaps your next construction project will be an HF transmitter capable of sending voice, not just Morse signals.

Amateurs can also send television pictures, either normal television or 'slow scan' television where it takes a few seconds to send one picture (rather like a fax machine), but sending or receiving world-wide.

Over 50 amateur satellites have been launched, usually piggy-backed on a commercial satellite launch or deployed by hand from the Space Shuttle.

Amateurs are still at the forefront of new radio developments. They do not have the money available to commercial organisations, but they do have the time and the ingenuity. A new mode of transmission, PSK31, was developed by amateurs. It uses a computer with a sound card to send and receive text by radio, under circumstances where most methods would be defeated by noise and interference.

Local radio clubs give talks on these developments, help and encourage new amateurs, train them to pass the higher category licence exams and provide social and operating 'on-air' evenings where new ideas can be tried out or just provide facilities that newcomers have not yet acquired.

Contests and 'field days' are opportunities to improve your operating skill, operate 'in the field', camping and enjoying radio at the same time. This activity is shared with Scout and Guide groups, and other youth groups such as the Air Training Corps.

A more serious side of the hobby is using amateur radio to provide communications for marathons or cross country runs. Also, particularly outside the major cities, in emergencies. Flooding and heavy snow falls do cause disruption to transport and communications. Telephones rely on the exchange not being flooded, and even cellular phones rely on an electricity supply to re-charge batteries and operate the cellular radio sites dotted around the country. Amateurs have their own equipment, ready charged batteries and the technical skill to set up communications in unusual or adverse conditions. They can provide communications when the normal methods have failed.

Why is there a training course?

ALTHOUGH A FORMAL COURSE is not compulsory it is highly recommended. All radio users require some form of training, even if it only extends to the protocols that allow messages to be passed quickly and accurately. That skill is useful for amateurs too. It gives a better impression to casual listeners, but the real reason is that amateurs are the only radio users permitted to build their own transmitting equipment. All other users must purchase ready made and approved devices, designed to allow them only certain facilities or frequencies.

Clearly the freedom that radio amateurs enjoy comes with a responsibility and the need for some technical capability, to ensure that home made equipment operates only within amateur bands and without causing interference to other radio users.

Foundation licensees are permitted to use commercially manufactured transmitters and kits constructed in accordance with the supplied instructions. Intermediate and Full licensees also have the privilege of building equipment to their own designs, from magazine articles, or modifying second hand commercial equipment. Ex-commercial equipment is often sold at radio rallies for a small fraction of its original cost, and represents a very cheap way of getting on the air.

It would be dangerous to allow Foundation licensees complete freedom for the simple reason that they are not sufficiently trained to be sure of building or modifying equipment so that it operates correctly on the amateur bands.

That extra freedom is an incentive for the Foundation licensee to upgrade, as are the extra transmit power and extra frequencies. Intermediate licensees may transmit at up to 50W of power and use additional frequencies. They can also send fast scan (normal) TV pictures. Full licensees may transmit up to 400W, have additional microwave bands, and may in certain circumstances apply for special permission to run even higher powers. Their licenses are also recognised in many other countries, European and world-wide which means that operation at sea is also permitted.

FLNC09

The Training Course

ATTENDING A TRAINING course is highly recommended although it is recognised that those already experienced in radio outside of Amateur Radio may be happy to self-study for the theoretical examination.

There are practical exercises and assessments that must be completed before the examination is taken. These exercises are included in formal courses both to help with understanding the coursework and to show that you are able to operate on-air correctly before getting your licence. Some Examination Centres may offer them as stand alone assessments as well as at relevant times during the training course. If you decide not to attend a course you are advised to ask your chosen club/Examination Centre how they conduct the practical exercises.

The course should last about 10-12 hours. Some courses will be run as two full days a week or fortnight apart and others over a few weeks, perhaps one evening a week and maybe a final day to finish. However it is run you will be able to sit a short written, multi-choice assessment at the end of the course. Your formal result will be posted to you about ten days later.

There is a small amount of theoretical work, but only enough for you to appreciate things like the correct fuse to use, the correct antenna to use, some basic theory to explain how your radio works and how to get the best out of your station. Safety is also a key part of the training.

You will be able to go on-line and obtain your own licence and call sign as soon as the papers have been returned to the RSGB and the results securely entered on Ofcom's licensing system. Alternatively a postal option is available but there is a fee for that option.

The course will show you different types of equipment, so you can start to decide what items you might like to get, what you can make, where the local clubs are and a bit about the national body for amateur radio, the Radio Society of Great Britain (RSGB).

The Practical Assessment

THE PRACTICAL ASSESSMENT is part of the training course and you will be given a Record of Achievement card, which you must get 'signed off' as you complete each item.

The completed card is needed to enter the Foundation examination, so don't loose it! If you sit (or re-sit) the exam at a later date, you will still need this card so keep it somewhere safe. You do not need to repeat the practical work but you are expected to sit or re-sit the exam within 12 months.

If you are unable to attend a course or choose to study on your own, you will still need to complete the practical assessments before sitting the exam.

Do not assume the exam includes the practical assessment; that is normally done as part of a training course. Because it involves on-air operating it must be supervised by a Full licensee who is a registered assessor able to sign your Record of Achievement card.

Your exam provider or the RSGB will be able to advise, but you do need to consider how you will complete the practical assessment when you start your studies.

The syllabus

YOU CAN OBTAIN a current issue of the syllabus from the RSGB web site. The aim of the syllabus is to cover those items necessary to allow amateurs on the air and to operate safely and in accordance with the customs and rules of amateur radio.

The syllabus includes sending and receiving Morse code; this is covered in the practical assessment. You do not need to memorise the code and the requirements are shown on page 31.

How do I find a training course?

THE QUICKEST WAY is to contact the RSGB and ask them for details of local courses or check their web site https://thersgb.org/services/clubfinder/ .

The tutors may run courses using their own personal station, the local amateur radio club may run a course, the Scouts, Guides or other organisations like the Air Training Corps may run one. The youth organisations are likely to run courses for their own members, but it is always worth asking.

If you are at school and your school does not run a course, suggest to someone that they do. The RSGB will be happy to advise on how this might be done and point to sources of assistance and training.

How much will it cost?

There is a charge for the exam and there may be a charge for the training course and practical assessment, hire of a hall for example. It is best to ask before committing to attend, but the costs should not be high and certainly should not be a reason to miss out.

A lifetime of enjoyment awaits you when you go 'on the bands'. Expect to increase your knowledge of geography, learn more about electronics and radio, make new friends and discover new activities.

Materials & Information

Gear like this can get you contacts around the world, but it doesn't cost the earth!

BEFORE YOU can take to the air, you are going to need some equipment. It would also be helpful if you were to equip yourself with some of the free leaflets produced by Ofcom.

How about the cost of equipment?

THE COST OF BEING a radio amateur can vary enormously. New handheld transceivers can cost from under £100 to over £400, depending on facilities. Mobile equipment, designed for in-car use, but more often than not found in the home, can set you back anything from £200 to £1000.

Second-hand equipment is typically around half those prices, depending on age and condition. Often, the earlier and less sophisticated 'rigs' as they are called, are easier to operate and eminently suitable for Foundation use. A simple antenna is quite adequate to get started. A length of thin wire from the house to a pole or tree in the garden can give ranges of many thousands of miles.

Many clubs have equipment that they loan to new amateurs. Members will be happy to join you at one of the many radio rallies, all advertised in the amateur press, and advise you on a purchase.

However, perhaps the most exciting way to get started in the hobby is to build a kit. These can be inexpensive, fun to build, offer extra insights into how they work, and you can then say to the amateurs you are in contact with that you built your own transmitter or receiver. Many would say that that is what amateur radio is all about.

Check the web!

IF ANY updates, additions or corrections to this book are issued, they may be found at: www.rsgb.org/books/extra/foundation

Useful contacts

Ofcom

Ofcom Licensing Centre
Ofcom, 2a Southwark Bridge Road
London, SE1 9HA
Tel: 020 7981 3131
Fax: 020 7981 3333
E-mail licensingcentre@ofcom.org.uk
www.ofcom.org.uk

RSGB

Radio Society of Great Britain
Tel: 01234 832 700
Fax: 01234 831 496
E-mail ar.dept@rsgb.org.uk
www.rsgb.org

RSGB Books

A wide variety of amateur radio books are available from RSGB.
Tel: 01234 832 700
Fax: 01234 831 496
E-mail sales@rsgb.org.uk
www.rsgbshop.org

Technical Basics

ONE OF THE KEY differences between radio amateurs and other users of radio is that amateurs are interested in how radio works. Other users don't care much about how it works, as long as it does.

When mobile handheld phones first became available, the users wondered why they did not work out in the depths of the countryside, in a valley or in a tunnel. The fact that these telephones used radio, and radio waves could not penetrate tunnels or the basements of large buildings, was not understood.

At the Foundation level, most of the training is about how to use a radio with only a little emphasis on the technicalities. Training for the higher licence classes includes more of the technical theory of electronics and radio.

Units & Symbols

Current (symbol 'I')

The current is a measure of how much electricity is flowing. The unit of measurement is the Amp (A).

The current is actually made up of millions of small particles called electrons, which are electrically charged and move round the circuit 'carrying' the electricity.

These electrons need enough room to move and if a larger current is expected to flow, a larger diameter wire is used. A bedside lamp may have a relatively thin wire, but an electric kettle will have a thicker one because it will take more current.

How many symbols are there?

Quite a lot, but you only need to know about a few of them right now.

FLNC01

Potential Difference (symbol 'V')

It is the current, the moving electrons that carry the electrical energy around a circuit. The electrons get their energy from the battery or power supply. As the electrons pass through something such as a bulb, motor or a radio they transfer some of their energy to it. The energy that is transferred can make the bulb light up, the motor spin round or the radio make a sound.

The electrons have more energy when they enter a device such as a bulb than when they leave it. The Potential Difference across the device shows this difference in energy and is the energy being transferred to it. Very often it is simply called the 'Voltage'.

Potential Difference is measured in a unit called a 'Volt'. If we measure more Volts across a device it means the flow of electrons (the Current) is transferring more energy to that device.

A 4-cell battery has a potential difference of 6V. It will give the electrons four times as much energy as a single cell (1.5V) and will cause the electrons to flow more quickly.

Caution! If we use the mains to supply energy to a piece of equipment the Potential Difference is 230 Volts. This is quite enough energy to kill you or cause you serious injury.

Large and Small Units

The unit of length is the metre. A tall person might be almost 2 metres tall and a 8 year old child may be 1 metre tall.

A ruler is usually 30cm long. The 'c' stands for 'centi' and the 'm' for 'metre'. One centimetre is one hundredth of a metre. There are 100 centimetres in a metre. If 1 centimetre is 1/100 of a metre, this can also be written as 0·01 of a metre. The ruler is 30 times this length so it is 30×0·01 = 0·3 metre long.

The millimetre is even smaller, 10 times smaller than the centimetre. There are 1000 millimetres in a metre, so each millimetre is 0·001 of a metre.

Distances are often much greater than a metre and are often measured in kilometres. The kilometre is 1000 metres. From London to Edinburgh is 411 kilometres, often written as 411km. In me-

tres it would be 411,000 metres. It would also be 411,000,000 millimetres!

In the scientific world it is common to use either very large or very small units. To avoid needing lots of zeros, the measurements are given in a suitable sized unit. The ones needed for the Foundation licence are the **milli**, the **kilo** and the **Mega**.

The **milli** is one thousandth, 1/1000 or 0·001. The abbreviation is 'm'.

A small current is 5 milliamps or 5mA. That would be 0·005A.

A small voltage might be 350mV, or 0·35V.

A single cell battery is 1500mV, which should be written as 1·5V.

The **kilo** is one thousand times or 1,000. The abbreviation is 'k'.

A distance of 45,000 metres should be written as 45km.

A high voltage of 2,300V should be written as 2·3kV.

The **mega** is 1,000 times bigger than a kilo, or 1,000,000 times bigger than the basic unit. The abbreviation is 'M'. Don't confuse this with 'm'.

A flash of lightning may be 4,000,000V, or 4MV. It may also cause a momentary current of 8,000 Amps, or 8kA to flow.

Electrical circuits

AN ELECTRIC CIRCUIT is the name given to the way electrical devices are connected. By connecting a battery and a light bulb we make a circuit consisting of the battery, the bulb and two pieces of wire to make the connections.

This is easiest to describe using a drawing and to help with that we will need to know how to draw a battery and a bulb so they will be recognised. This is done by using standard symbols. The standard symbol for a battery is shown in **Fig 1**.

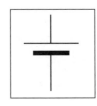

Fig 1: The circuit symbol for a single cell. The longer side is the positive connection.

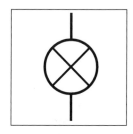

Fig 2: The circuit symbol for a light bulb. There is no polarity for a filament bulb, so it can be connected either way around.

The battery provides the electrical energy. It has two connections, a positive connection and a negative connection. The electricity flows out of the positive connection along the connecting wire, through the bulb and back along the lower wire to the battery's negative connection. Electricity, unlike water, needs a complete circuit or path to flow round. There must be a continuous route from the positive side of the battery round the circuit and back to the negative side. The route is completed inside the battery.

A single cell provides about 1·5 volts of 'push', or electrical potential, to cause the electricity to flow. More cells can be connected together to provide a higher voltage or 'potential difference' (p.d.).

Some electrical or electronic devices are very sensitive to which way round the battery is connected. The two connections of the battery are sometimes called its poles, and connecting them the right way round is called the correct 'polarity'.

A light bulb (**Fig 2**) is a thin filament of wire in a glass bulb where all the air has been sucked out, ie a vacuum. If electricity is passed through the bulb the filament glows white hot and gives off heat and light. It does not matter which way the electricity passes through the bulb, so the bulb does not have a polarity to worry about.

In **Fig 3** you will see that the battery, a single cell, has now been connected to the bulb to form a battery and bulb circuit. The bulb will light.

Care must be taken to ensure the battery is of the correct voltage for the bulb, or it will either be too dim or too bright and possibly 'blow'.

Conductors & Insulators

The connecting wire we use to join the battery to the bulb is a conductor, it conducts electricity because the electrons can move freely. Metals are conductors. The wire should also have a plastic sheath or covering. That is an insulator which does not conduct electricity. The electrons cannot move in an insulator. Wood, rubber, glass and ceramics are also insulators but if they get wet, the electricity may be able to flow through the surface water and still give you a nasty shock. It is wise to be very careful in wet conditions.

Power & Resistance

THERE ARE TWO other electrical units we need to consider.

Power

When a current flows through a device the electrons transfer some of their energy to it. Bulbs light up, motors spin and a radio will make a sound.

If we think about this a little more we can see that to make the bulb brighter, the motor spin faster or the radio louder, the energy has to be transferred more quickly.

To deliver the energy more rapidly we can do two things.

a) Give the electrons more energy. We do this by using a battery or power supply with more Volts ie, a greater potential difference.

b) Increase the rate at which the electrons move around the circuit. In other words we increase the Current flowing in the circuit.

Power is a measure of how quickly the device transfers the energy we deliver to it. As the bulb gets brighter, the motor spins faster and radio gets louder we say they are absorbing more POWER and working harder. A powerful device is transferring a great deal of energy each second. Working out the Power absorbed:

Power (Watts) = Potential Difference (V) x Current (I)

$$P = V \times I$$

The PD tells us how much energy each electron has and the current tells us how many electrons are arriving each second to transfer their energy. Multiplying V and I tells us how much energy is arriving and how quickly it is being transferred, it tells us the Power being absorbed by the device.

We measure Power in a Unit called a Watt. A one Watt bulb transfers one unit of energy every second to heat and light. A 1kW kettle will take twice as long to boil as a 2kW kettle if they both have the same amount of water.

Examples of power calculations are shown in the shaded panel above.

Resistance

Resistance is a measure of how difficult it is for electricity to flow. The symbol for resistance is 'R' and it is measured in ohms (symbol 'Ω', the Greek letter omega).

The concept of resistance may be easier to visualize if you are filling the paddling pool using a hose. A young child stands on the hose. The flow of water reduces. The hose has been

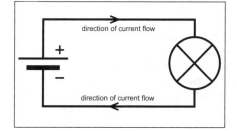

Fig 3: A single cell battery and bulb circuit.

slightly squashed, which caused some difficulty or resistance to the water flowing. The water has not been cut off, but the flow (current) has been reduced.

You have two choices. You can ask the child to step off the hose, or you may be able to turn the tap on further to increase the flow of water back to where is was.

In removing the child from the hose, you have removed the resistance, so the flow has increased. In turning the tap on further you have increased the water potential, pushing more water through the hose. Either way you are now filling the pool as quickly as before. If you had chosen to turn the tap on further, you might have a different problem if the child then steps off the hose, but that is another matter.

In electrical terms, a device that restricts the flow of current is called a 'resistor'. How much difficulty it presents to the flow of current is called its resistance. This corresponds to the weight of the child standing on the hose.

A resistor of higher value will offer more resistance or difficulty to the flow of current. If the voltage stays the same then a higher resistance will result in a lower current flowing.

Increasing the voltage (like turning the tap further on) will give the electrons more energy, causing an increase in the current.

Clearly the voltage, the current and the resistance are related somehow. An increase in voltage causes an increase in current and an increase in resistance causes a decrease in current.

The actual relationship is:

$$\text{Current (I)} = \frac{\text{Voltage (V)}}{\text{Resistance (R)}}$$

This relationship was first set out clearly in 1826 by a physics teacher in Cologne, George Simon Ohm. The relationship is named after him.

Ohm's Law

THE CURRENT flowing through a circuit is directly proportional to the applied voltage and inversely proportional to the resistance. A useful way of remembering this is shown in **Fig 4**.

Referring again to Fig 4, if you place a finger over the item you wish to calculate, the formula for the calculation is shown by the remaining quantities. **Fig 5** demonstrates this.

Examples of calculations using Ohms Law are shown in the panel above.

---

1. A torch bulb has a resistance of 10 ohms, and is designed to run at 3V. What current will flow when correctly connected?

   The formula to use is: $\text{Current (I)} = \dfrac{\text{Voltage (V)}}{\text{Resistance (R)}}$

   So, inserting the numbers... $\text{Current (I)} = \dfrac{3}{10} = 0.3\text{A}$

2. For the electric fire, we were told it ran on 230V and drew 10A. What is its resistance?

   The formula to use is: $\text{Resistance (R)} = \dfrac{\text{Voltage (V)}}{\text{Current (I)}}$

   So, inserting the numbers... $\text{Resistance (R)} = \dfrac{230}{10} = 23\Omega$

Uses for resistors

So far we have looked at the resistance of items such as light bulbs and electric fires.

In electronic circuits it is often necessary to deliberately limit the flow of current. To do this a device called a resistor is used to insert some resistance into the circuit. The circuit symbol for a resistor is a rectangular box. This is shown in **Fig 6** and is marked 'R'.

A low value resistor will have little effect on the flow of current and the bulb will glow quite brightly. A higher value of resistor will have a greater limiting effect on the current, and the bulb will then be much less bright. If the resistor value is too high, the bulb may not glow at all.

In Fig 6, let us say there is a choice of values for the resistor R. The choices are: 1Ω, 2Ω, 5Ω and 10Ω (remember, Ω is

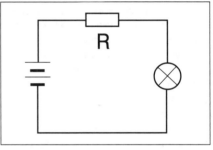

Fig 6: An electric circuit with some added resistance.

ohms). Which value of resistor will allow the bulb to glow the brightest?

The lower the value of the resistor, the less it limits the flow of current, so the lowest value will give the brightest glow. Therefore, choose the 1Ω resistor.

Alternating currents & Voltages

SO FAR WE HAVE looked at the current flowing from a battery. It flows out of the positive terminal, round the circuit, the bulb or whatever, and back to the negative terminal. The electricity always flows the same way. It is called 'direct current' (DC or d.c.) because it always flows in the same direction.

Alternating current (AC or a.c.) is different. It keeps on changing direction, first one way and then the other.

AC is easier to generate and easier to change from one voltage to another. The mains electricity supply to the house is alternating current. The generator at the power station is a large coil of wire rotating in a powerful magnetic field. If we look at just one wire in the rotating coil, it is first going up through the field, then, half a turn later, coming down.

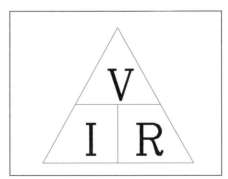

Fig 4: The relationship between voltage (V), current (I) and resistance (R).

$$I = \frac{V}{R} \qquad V = I \times R \qquad R = \frac{V}{I}$$

Fig 5: The formulae for calculating current (I), voltage (V) and resistance (R).

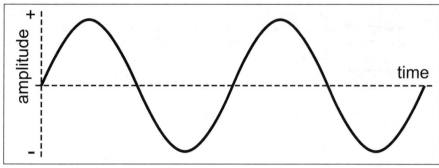

Fig 7: A graph showing the varying value of voltage and current over time for an AC waveform.

Frequency	Wavelength
1MHz	300 metres
3 MHz	100 metres
10MHz	30 metres
30MHz	10 metres
100MHz	3 metres
300MHz	1 metre
1000MHz	30 cms

Table 2: Frequency versus wavelength

Whilst the wire is going up the voltage and current generated has one polarity and moments later when the wire is coming down the voltage and current are of opposite polarity.

The alternator in a car produces AC, but that is no use to charge the car battery or to run many of the electronic items in the car such as the radio. Special electronics are needed to convert the alternating current to direct current. That re-charges the car battery and powers all the car electrical items including the lights (which could use AC or DC).

The same electronics to convert AC to DC in a car is also needed in mains driven electronic equipment, such as televisions. There may also be a need to change the 230V mains to a lower voltage. That is easy to do with AC, using a transformer. It is not nearly so simple with a DC supply. The methods of doing that are covered in the Intermediate and Full amateur licence courses.

Alternating currents and voltages do not suddenly switch from one polarity to the other. As **Fig 7** shows, they build up to a peak in one direction, then reduce back to zero before building up in the opposite direction. This smooth waveform is known as a 'sine wave' (from the sine function in trigonometry).

There are two features of an alternating current or voltage that we need to know. Not only do we need to know the size of the voltage, we also need to know how often the cycles of change occur. That is called the frequency. Frequency is defined as the number of cycles occurring in one second. The unit of measurement is cycles per second or 'Hertz' (Hz).

The domestic mains supply is 230 volts and 50Hz. That means there are 50 complete cycles in one second. Fig 7 shows two complete cycles.

Different frequencies

SOUND IS ALSO an alternating signal. As sound, the signal is carried by the movement of air. A sound of 50 cycles per second (50Hz) is a very low note, as much felt as it is heard.

Human hearing ranges from about 100Hz (a low note) to 15kHz (a very high note). As we get older the upper limit drops, and adults may have difficulty above 10kHz. Many animals, eg dogs, can hear much higher frequencies.

For high quality music the full range of frequencies is desirable, but for speech a much narrower range is quite sufficient. It is usually considered that the range for pleasant communication is about 300Hz to 3kHz. That is typical of a good telephone line. Mobile telephones are a bit poorer, and many people can clearly hear the difference.

Electrical signals in the leads to a loudspeaker are alternating currents and voltages, and many frequencies may be present at the same time, depending on the sounds. A clean whistle will be a single note and a single electrical frequency, whilst a piece of music is likely to contain many notes and hence many frequencies.

Radio frequencies (RF)

RADIO WAVES ARE generated by feeding alternating electrical signals to an aerial (often called an antenna). The frequencies of radio waves are much higher than those we can hear.

For ease of reference, the wide range of radio frequencies are divided into bands (see **Table 1**).

The amateur frequencies of most interest to Foundation amateurs are in the HF, VHF and UHF bands. They are shown in the schedule to the amateur licence. There is also a small band at 137kHz, used mostly for research into how radio waves propagate at those frequencies.

Wavelength

THE WAVELENGTH of a wave is the distance between the same point on two consecutive cycles.

Consider waves in the sea. Two peaks might be about 10 metres apart. If the waves are more frequent they will be closer together. Therefore, the frequency and the wavelength are related. A higher frequency gives a shorter wavelength. **Table 2** shows the relationship between various frequencies and wavelengths.

Fig 8 will convert from Frequency in MHz to wavelength in metres. The symbol for wavelength is the Greek letter lambda, λ.

Frequency range	Band	Name
300kHz – 3MHz	MF	Medium frequencies or "medium wave band"
3MHz – 30MHz	HF	High frequencies or HF band
30MHz – 300MHz	VHF	Very high frequencies or VHF band
300MHz – 3000MHz	UHF	Ultra high frequencies or UHF band

Table 1: You should remember the frequency ranges of the HF, VHF and UHF bands.

To convert from frequency to wavelength, select a point on the 'X' (horizontal) axis of the graph, say 100MHz, and look vertically upwards until your reach the diagonal line. Now look horizontally to the 'Y' (vertical) axis to read off the wavelength, in this case 3 metres.

To convert from wavelength to frequency, start with the wavelength on the vertical axis, 40 metres for example. Look along horizontally to the diagonal line and then vertically down to the 'X' axis. Read off 7·5MHz. A radio wave of wavelength 40 metres has a frequency of 7·5MHz.

To be sure that you read the graph correctly, it may be helpful to mark the number you are given (frequency or wavelength) on the axis and then draw the two lines.

Other radio users

AMATEURS SHARE the use of radio and the radio spectrum with many other users. Sometimes the other users are on adjacent frequencies and, where it is possible to do so, amateurs share frequencies with other users.

Table 3 shows other radio users in part of the VHF band.

Amateurs occupy 144·0 to 146·0MHz, often called the 2 metre band because the wavelength is about 2 metres.

The band from 87·5 to 108·0MHz is shown as Broadcasting. It is the VHF FM broadcast band, containing national and local radio stations.

Adjacent to the amateur allocation is the Land Mobile band from 138·0 to 144·0MHz and above is the Mobile except aeronautical mobile band. The Land mobile band is for the use of land based mobile transmitters, vehicles or pedestrians, and the band 146·0 to 149·9MHz may be used by land or sea based transmitters but not from aircraft.

A typical exam question will ask who has the use of a particular band or who a user is next to in the table. It is worth reading the table a few times but there is no need to memorise it. This table will be provided, as will the Frequency to Wavelength chart, even if there is no question on that topic!

Frequency			Use
87·5	-	108·0MHz	Broadcasting
108·0	-	117·975MHz	Aeronautical Radionavigation
117·975	-	137·0MHz	Aeronautical Mobile
137·0	-	138·0MHz	Space Operations & Space Research
138·0	-	144·0MHz	Land Mobile
144·0	-	*146·0MHz*	*Amateur & Amateur Satellite*
146·0	-	149·9MHz	Mobile (except aeronautical mobile)
149·9	-	150·05MHz	Radionavigation-Satellite
150·05	-	152·0MHz	Radio Astronomy
152·0	-	156·0MHz	Land Mobile
156·0	-	158·525MHz	Maritime Mobile
158·525	-	160·6MHz	Land Mobile
160·6	-	160·975MHz	Maritime Mobile

Table 3: The various uses of part of the VHF band of frequencies.

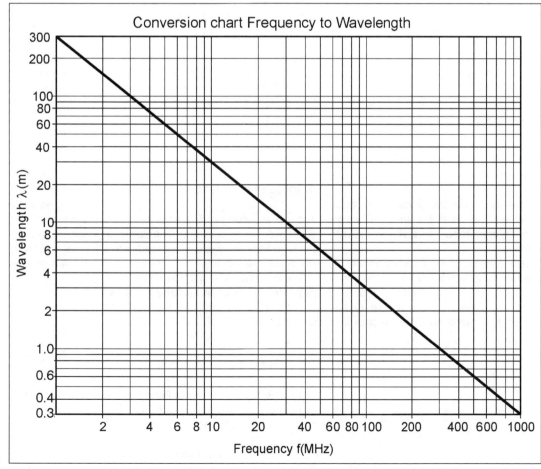

Fig 8: Graph to convert frequency to wavelength (or wavelength to frequency).

Transmitters

THE TRANSMITTER is an important piece of equipment in your 'shack'. The reason it is important is that it generates radio waves and if there is a problem, the radio signal might cause difficulty to another radio user who may or may not be an amateur.

For this reason, as an amateur, it is necessary for you to understand a bit about how the transmitter works.

Simple transmitter

A SIMPLE TRANSMITTER consists only of a method of generating the correct radio frequency, plus an antenna (or aerial). To send messages it is necessary to switch the transmitter 'on' and 'off' in an arranged way. Morse code is the most well known code which is able to send the letters of the alphabet, numbers and punctuation marks, simply by switching on and off. The need to send voice (or pictures) meant that a method of superimposing information on the radio signal had to be devised. The device to do that is known as a 'modulator'.

One way of showing the basic functions inside a transmitter and how they connect together is to draw a block diagram (see **Fig 9**).

1. Audio stage
2. Modulator
3. Frequency Generator (oscillator)
4. RF Power Amplifier

The symbol on the left of the diagram is a microphone.

The signal from the microphone is quite weak and needs to be amplified in the audio stage, shown as box 1 in the diagram.

Box 3 is the Frequency Generator. It produces the frequency which the transmitter will use to transmit the signal. The frequency generator must be carefully designed and made so as to be sure it is working on the correct frequency. Transmission on the wrong frequency will mean that the person you are talking to will not be able to hear you. But, far more importantly, you will be transmitting on somebody else's frequency, possibly outside the amateur bands. That could cause considerable problems to other users, especially if their messages are important or concern safety.

Box 2 is the 'Modulator' which takes the radio signal from box 3 and mixes it with the audio signal from box 1 to produce a modulated radio signal.

This signal is usually not powerful enough to transmit, so an 'RF Power Amplifier' amplifies the signal. This is shown in box 4.

This strong signal is now fed to the antenna, shown by this symbol.

Modulation

THE PROCESS OF getting the radio signal to carry an audio signal is called 'modulation'. The radio signal before modulation is added is often called the 'carrier'.

There are two simple ways of modulating a carrier. The first is to vary the amplitude of the carrier in time with the audio signal. This is called 'Amplitude Modulation' or 'AM'. The other way is to vary the frequency of the carrier in time with the audio signal. This is called 'Frequency Modulation' or 'FM'.

Amplitude Modulation

The top waveform of **Fig 10** is the audio signal from a microphone. The carrier is the high frequency (closer spaced) wave of constant amplitude.

The process of amplitude modulation produces a wave of the same frequency as the carrier, but its amplitude varies in time with the audio signal.

Frequency Modulation

The top waveform of **Fig 11** is the signal from a microphone. The steady, high frequency wave is the carrier.

Frequency modulation produces a modulated wave of constant amplitude, but with the frequency

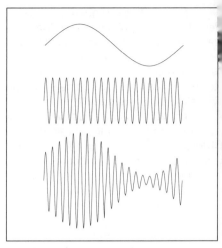

Fig 10: An Amplitude Modulated signal.

varying in time with the signal from the microphone. The frequency does not vary much, and the radio receiver is tuned to the centre of the frequency variations of the signal.

Care must be taken with either type of modulation not to 'over-modulate', that is not to have too strong a signal from the microphone and audio stage feeding the modulator. That is usually caused by turning the 'microphone gain' up too far. The effect is similar to turning up the volume on the receiver, except that the effects are heard at the distant end of the radio contact. Shouting into the microphone might also cause problems.

Excessive amplitude modulation will make the peaks of the modulated carrier too large and reduce the troughs to zero. This will distort the audio, which will sound rough in the receiver. It will also cause interference to radio receivers tuned to adjacent channels, which it is particularly important to avoid. It is a condition of your licence that you do not cause interference to other radio users.

Excessive frequency modulation is also undesirable and may cause interference to neighbouring users, as well as risking poor quality audio signals for your intended recipient.

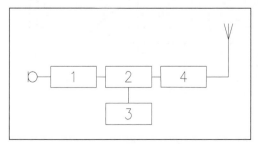

Fig 9: Block diagram of a simple transmitter.

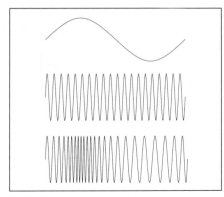

Fig 11: A Frequency Modulated signal.

Receivers

THE RECEIVER MUST pick up the weak radio signals, select the right signal from the thousands of different transmitters located all over the world, amplify it to a suitable level, extract the audio (or data or picture) from the modulated waveform and then present it to us in a suitable form.

Outside and inside the MFJ Cub, a complete transceiver that you build from a kit.

Simple receiver

The block diagram of a receiver is shown in **Fig 12**.

1. Tuning and RF amplifier
2. Detection
3. Audio amplifier
4. Loudspeaker

The radio signal is picked up by the antenna, now converting a radio wave into electrical signals on the feeder, and fed along the feeder to the input of the receiver, box 1.

Box 1 contains the tuning, which selects the wanted signal from all the hundreds of signals picked up by the antenna, and RF amplification which amplifies the wanted signal to bring it up to a suitable level to be used by box 2.

Box 2 contains the detector, which recovers the original modulating signal. It extracts the original audio signal from the modulated signal, as the carrier is no longer required. Detection is often also called de-modulation.

Box 3 contains an audio amplifier, which ensures the audio signal is powerful enough to drive the loudspeaker or headphones.

The wanted radio signal is selected by tuning the receiver to the correct frequency. You will learn how 'tuned circuits' achieve this in the Intermediate training course. You will also cover how a transistor can amplify the signal, making it strong enough to use. For now it is sufficient to know that the circuits in the receiver shown in Box 1 perform those functions.

Detector

THE TYPE OF detector used must be suitable for the method of modulation being used at the transmitter. This can be demonstrated using an amateur radio receiver by setting the 'mode' switch to the wrong type of modulation.

The mode switch is discussed in more detail in the section on operating and during the practical training. The correct mode needs to be chosen to correctly recover the original audio signal. The technical details of other types of modulation are covered in the Intermediate and Advanced courses.

If it was a data signal sent at the transmitter then again a suitable detector is needed and the selection of the correct mode (eg upper or lower sideband or FM) is just as important but might be harder to determine by ear. The operating chapter has more details.

For the exam, questions on receivers will assume a loudspeaker is being used as shown in Fig 12.

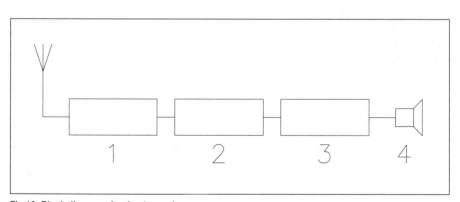

Fig 12: Block diagram of a simple receiver.

Feeders &Antennas

Feeders

THE WIRE connecting a transmitter to an antenna or aerial is called the feeder.

The feeder is carrying powerful radio frequency signals which will radiate from any piece of wire. To prevent radiation from the feeder, it is usually made as coaxial cable (**Fig 13**). A coaxial cable contains a centre conductor, which carries the signal, and an outer screen. The primary purpose of the screen is to confine the signal within the cable.

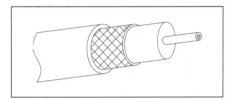

Fig 13: Coaxial cable is the type of cable used on a TV antenna.

The outer screen is usually braided to provide a good, continuous covering. The inner conductor may be a single, thick piece of wire, or a few twisted strands.

The correct type of plug must be used, either a 'BNC' or a 'PL259'. These are illustrated in **Fig 14**. The screen of the coaxial cable must be properly connected to the body of the plug to ensure the screen and plug form a continuous shield for the inner conductor, which is soldered to the centre pin in the plug.

Antennas

THE ANTENNA (sometimes called an aerial) actually radiates the signal. It converts the electrical signals on the feeder into radio waves.

It needs to be designed for the frequency or wavelength in use. There are five antennas that we need to consider for the Foundation exam. Once you are licensed the choice of antenna is entirely up to you.

The dipole

The dipole is the basic antenna and is half a wavelength long. This means the size of the dipole (and all other antennas) must be suitable for the intended frequency of use.

If it is mounted vertically, as shown in **Fig 15**, it radiates equally in all horizontal directions. If it is mounted horizontally, which is more common at HF, it radiates well from the sides but not off the ends. Given the choice, it should be side-on to the desired direction of maximum signal, but this is not always possible in a small garden.

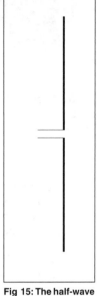

Fig 15: The half-wave dipole antenna.

The ¼ wave ground plane

This antenna gets its name from the fact that the radiating element is ¼ wavelength long, often written as λ/4 since the symbol for wavelength is the Greek letter λ, lambda.

The radiating or active element is always vertical (see **Fig 16**). The 4 horizontal wires, called 'radials', form a 'ground plane' - an earthed surface which acts like a mirror to radio waves.

The transmitted signal is 'omni-directional', that is it radiates equally in all horizontal directions. It does not radiate vertically.

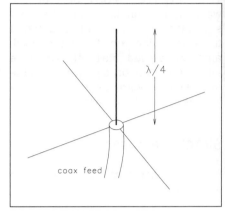

Fig 16: The λ/4 ground plane antenna.

The Yagi

The Yagi antenna is directional. Most TV antennas are Yagis, mounted to point at the TV transmitter. The antenna is able to focus the radio signal in a particular direction, in much the same way as a searchlight or car headlight beams the light in one direction.

Maximum signal is towards the tapering end. In **Fig 17** this is to the right. The Yagi can be mounted with the elements vertical (as shown), or horizontally. For good communication the transmit and receive Yagis must point towards each other and be either both horizontal or both vertical. It is worth noting that the thicker vertical line is actually a dipole, which must be half a wavelength long.

The Yagi is a useful antenna because of its focussing ability. The signal transmitted in the wanted direction is increased, whilst that in other directions is reduced. Greater range can be achieved or a lower transmit power could be used. The effective power in the wanted direction has increased by the focussing 'gain' of the antenna. This gain is usually quoted by the manufacturer.

The 'effective radiated power' or 'erp' is

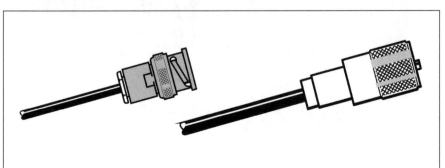

Fig 14: Left, a BNC plug. Right, a PL259. Note that the PL259 is somewhat larger.

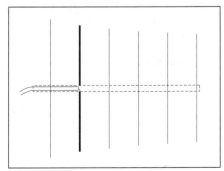

Fig 17: The Yagi antenna.

A large yagi antenna, mounted on a tower.

Gain (dB)	Gain (times)
3	2
6	4
9	8
10	10

Table 4: The gain of an antenna is usually expressed in decibels.

the product of the actual transmit power and the gain of the antenna.

erp = antenna gain × transmit power

Unfortunately, most manufacturers quote antenna gain in a scientific way, using units called decibels (dB). This can be converted to actual gain by using **Table 4**.

The 5/8-wave ground plane

This is a development of the ¼-wave ground plane. It is better at directing signals

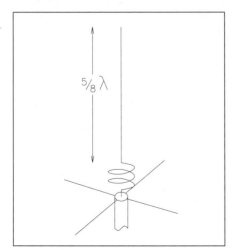

Fig 18: The 5/8 wave ground plane antenna.

towards the horizon, rather than up in the air. It is always mounted with the active element vertical and is omni-directional.

As **Fig 18** shows, the vertical active element is 5/8 of a wavelength long. Due to the size, this type of antenna is most often used on VHF and UHF frequencies, where wavelengths are shorter.

The coil at the base is part of the matching of the antenna to the coaxial cable. Matching is described later.

The end-fed

This antenna (shown in **Fig 19**) is easy to provide for HF use, where the wavelengths may well be longer than the garden. It is unlikely to be either ¼ or ½ wavelength long and matching will be a problem. A device called an 'antenna tuning unit' (ATU) will allow for this and enable the antenna to accept power from the transmitter.

The antenna is often set up with the far end fixed to a pole or a tree and the end closest to the house secured by a short insulated rope to the chimney or suitable fixing, with the end dropping down the side of the house connecting to the transmitter. Unfortunately, this results in high voltages or high currents close to the house and the strong radiation is quite likely to upset the television or other electronic equipment, including neighbours' equipment. If such an antenna is unavoidable, it is better to feed it at the far end using a buried feeder. This is discussed later in 'EMC'.

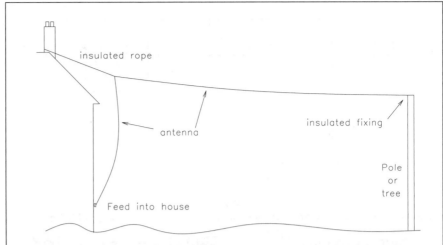

Fig 19: How a long wire antenna can be connected from the house to a tree or pole in the garden.

Polarisation.

THE POLARISATION OF an antenna means which way up it is. The Yagi mentioned earlier could be mounted either horizontally or vertically. The polarisation of the antenna also determines the polarisation of the radio wave. For all the antennas we have seen here, the polarisation of the wave is the same as the 'live' element of the antenna. A vertical dipole or Yagi will radiate a vertical radio wave. It will also best receive vertical waves.

It does not matter much which polarisation is chosen as long as both antennas are the same. However, Ground Plane and 5/8 antennas are always vertical. Mobile antennas mounted on a vehicle are vertical for practical reasons.

There is an amateur convention at VHF and UHF that when using FM the antenna is vertical (most mobile operation uses FM) and SSB operation uses horizontal polarisation.

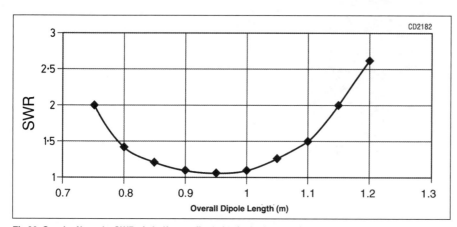

Fig 20: Graph of how the SWR of a half wave dipole for the 2m band varies as the length of the legs is varied.

Matching antennas

IF THE SIZE OF the antenna is correct, ½ wavelength long at the wanted frequency if it is a dipole, for example, then the antenna will match the transmitter and feeder. This means that the power from the transmitter will be properly radiated by the antenna. If the antenna is used on the wrong frequency, so that it is not the correct size, some of the power will be reflected back down the feeder instead of being radiated by the antenna.

A similar effect can be seen in a pool, where a wave is reflected by the side of the pool.

Antenna Tuning Unit (ATU)

THE ATU IS A device that can be fitted in the feeder, usually at the transmitter end for convenience, that can cope with any power reflected by the antenna and allow the transmitter to send the power to the antenna and for the antenna to radiate it well.

An ATU is quite common in HF installations, where a single antenna often has to be used for several bands due to space limitations. The antenna will only match well on one band. All the others will be a compromise and an ATU will be needed for good results. Without an ATU, if the mis-match is severe, the transmitter could be damaged. Alternatively, protection devices in the transmitter will reduce or shut down the power.

Standing waves and SWR meters

IF SOME OF the RF power is reflected at the antenna, this will mix with the power going up the feeder and cause an effect called 'standing waves'. The waves travelling up the feeder combine with those reflected down, to give the appearance of stationary or standing waves.

An SWR (standing wave ratio) meter can measure the power flowing back down the feeder, allowing the operator to adjust the ATU until the antenna system is matched and the reflected power to the transmitter is minimised.

If the reading on the SWR meter has unexpectedly increased, it means that more signal is being reflected back from the antenna. The most likely cause is some damage to the antenna. Possibly it has suffered in the wind or been hit by a large bird. The cause should be investigated before continuing to transmit.

A dipole antenna is a good match only when cut to the correct length. At other lengths the match will be poorer, depending on how far from the ideal length it is. **Fig 20** shows the effect of varying the length of the two halves of a dipole.

In your practical assessment, you will set up an adjustable dipole, a transmitter and an SWR meter. The dipole will probably be made using two extendible aerials like those found on small portable broadcast radios.

If the dipole is too short, corresponding to the left side of Fig 20, the SWR will be high. Gradually lengthen the two halves, keeping them equal, checking the SWR after each adjustment. The power will be low, but do not adjust the dipole whilst transmitting.

You should come to a point where the SWR is a minimum. Note the length of the dipole but continue the experiment, making the dipole longer each time.

It is not usual to have an ATU for the VHF and UHF bands (which is where you will conduct this experiment), but, if you did have one, it would be possible to set the dipole to the wrong length, insert the ATU and adjust it to make the transmitter think the dipole was correct. The SWR will appear low to the transmitter, which will then work quite happily.

Baluns

LOOK CAREFULLY AGAIN at the dipole antenna. The dipole is symmetrical, that is to say the two halves are the same. It is called a 'balanced' antenna and requires two signals, one for each half of the dipole. The signals are balanced because when the wave on one side is going up, the wave on the other side is going down (rather like a balanced see-saw).

A coaxial cable is not electrically symmetrical and is called 'unbalanced'. It has one centre 'live' conductor and an earthed screen. It is not suitable to directly feed a dipole. A device called a balun (balanced to unbalanced transformer) takes the signal on the coaxial cable and converts it to two signals suitable for feeding the dipole.

If the coaxial cable is connected directly to a dipole, RF current will flow back down the screen of the cable. This current will radiate, and the screening properties of the cable will be upset. Since the cable runs back into the house, radiation will take place inside the house and may cause some interference to the television or other electronic devices. This must be avoided.

Dummy loads

A DUMMY LOAD is a carefully constructed resistor, capable of absorbing all the power from the transmitter and presenting a good match, ie no power is reflected. It must also be well screened, to minimise any unwanted radiation. This allows the transmitter to be set up and tested without radiating any significant power.

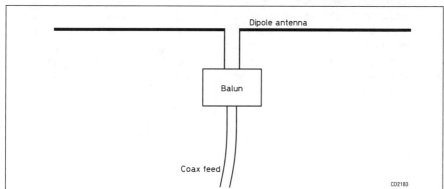

Fig 21: Insert a balun at the point where coaxial cable meets a dipole antenna.

Propagation

PROPAGATION IS THE technical term for how radio waves behave once they have left the transmitting antenna.

Radio waves and light waves both belong to a larger family of waves called electromagnetic waves. The term also includes x-rays and many cosmic rays.

Like light, radio waves travel in straight lines unless they are reflected off a suitable surface or are refracted, that is bent in the same way that light is bent in a prism or lens.

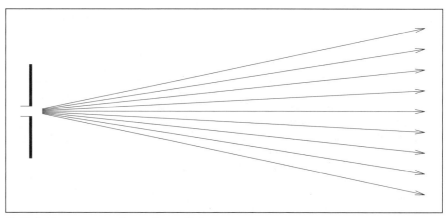

Fig 22: Radio waves, spreading out from a dipole antenna.

Spreading out

RADIO WAVES ALSO spread out from the antenna, as shown in **Fig 22**.

Close to the antenna they are concentrated, so a receiving antenna will pick up a strong signal. Further away the signal will be weaker. Too far away and the signal will be too weak to be received. The effect is the same as shining a torch beam onto a wall. Close to the wall there is a clear, bright circle of light. As the torch is moved further away the light is more spread out and appears weaker. If moved sufficiently far away, it is not visible at all.

Buildings

RADIO WAVES CAN penetrate buildings in much the same way as an x-ray will pass through the skin, but bones will leave a shadow. Some of the energy is lost in penetrating the building. In the basement or in the middle of a large building, where there are several walls to pass through, the signal may be too weak to be of use.

The penetrating ability of radio waves depends very much on their frequency. For lower frequencies in the medium wave and HF bands, the wavelengths are large and the buildings 'appear' fairly small in comparison. Such waves penetrate buildings quite easily, but have difficulty with mountains. At higher frequencies, in the VHF and UHF bands, the wavelengths are much shorter and the buildings comparatively bigger. The same building is much more of a problem to VHF and UHF waves than it is for HF.

There is one small advantage for the higher frequencies; if the wavelength is smaller than a window, the window appears as a big enough hole for it to get through. There is then a reasonable signal in a room with a window on the side facing the transmitter.

The best range with VHF and UHF radio services is achieved when the transmit antenna is mounted high up and clear of local obstructions such as trees and buildings. It helps greatly if the receiving antenna is also sited in a similar way.

Broadcast transmitters have very tall masts supporting the antenna for just that reason. It also helps in getting the signal into the dips behind hills and into valleys. Such places would otherwise be in a bit of a shadow. This effect can be seen on a clear day when the sun is just rising or setting. Even a relatively small hill causes a long shadow, which disappears as soon as the sun is higher in the sky.

Range

THE RANGE achieved depends on a number of factors. Clearly, a more powerful transmitter will have a greater range. However, the effect is not as noticeable as might be expected. Consider the torch beam again. At double the distance the circle of light is twice as wide and twice as high. It has 4 times the area to cover, so each bit of wall only gets a quarter of the light. To get the same strength as before the beam must be four times as powerful, not twice.

In amateur terms, it is much more effective to use a yagi antenna to focus all the transmitted power in the right direction, than getting a bigger transmitter. Also, the antenna 'gain' is effective on receive, giving us a more sensitive receiver.

Even that is not always the best option, although it is a very good one because it also avoids sending transmit power in all the wrong directions. The best option, as mentioned previously, is to get the transmit and receive antennas clear of the clutter and above the roof tops. Use a yagi as well and you will have a very capable station.

Frequency affects the range. The higher the frequency, the bigger the buildings and trees appear to the radio wave, and the more the wave is lost in penetrating them. Hills cause shadows and the curvature of the earth also has an effect in making any hills in the middle of the path seem taller. At VHF, and even more so at UHF, the range is not much further than line-of-sight. Depending on the terrain, that may be anything from 10 or 20 km up to 60 to 80km in open country from a hilltop. Between handheld radios, down amongst buildings, even 1km may prove difficult.

The ionosphere

THE IONOSPHERE is the name given to layers of partially conductive gas occurring at heights between 70 and 400 km above the earth. These layers are formed by the action of ultra-violet light from the sun, interacting with the air molecules in the upper atmosphere. The details are considered in the Intermediate and Full licence courses.

For Foundation purposes it is sufficient to note that the strength or level of ionisation of the ionosphere varies with the time of day, that is the amount of sunlight. It also varies with the season, ie from summer to winter.

The ionosphere can refract or bend radio waves in the same way as a lens bends light. To see this effect in light, hold a pencil or drinking straw at an angle in a bowl of water and look through the water at the straw. It appears bent at the point it enters the water. It isn't, of course. What has happened is that the light is bent on entering the water, so the wet part of the straw appears to be in a slightly different position.

As **Fig 23** shows, radio waves travelling up towards the ionosphere may be bent or refracted back to the earth's surface some thousands of kilometres from the transmitter.

The key point about this is that the

FLNC05

signal can now be heard far over the horizon and well beyond the range that would be achieved by a wave travelling direct to the receiver.

Frequency & time of day

THIS EFFECT IS frequency dependent. When the ionosphere is strong or highly ionised, it can bend higher frequencies back to earth than when it is weak. During the day frequencies as high as 30MHz or more may be returned, whereas during the night this may be as low as 3MHz. In the summer the highs and lows are more modest. In the winter the highs are often higher and the lows lower.

The highest frequency that will return to earth is known as the Maximum Usable Frequency (MUF). As just explained, the MUF depends on time of day and the season. Amateur radio magazines often give a prediction of the MUF for the month, so the amateur can decide which HF band offers the best chance of a contact. Ideally the band chosen should be a bit below the MUF.

Any one band may only offer contacts for a few hours each day. The band is said to be 'open'. As the morning progresses it may be necessary to move up one or two bands until early afternoon, when it may be necessary to move back down a bit. Further moves down in frequency will be needed as the evening and night progress.

World-wide propagation is possible by ionospheric or 'sky wave' paths. A single hop can travel up to 4000km. The radio wave can bounce off the earth's surface, allowing multiple hops and world-wide coverage. Part of the fun and skill in amateur radio is knowing which bands to use, at which time, and where is likely to be reached for a contact.

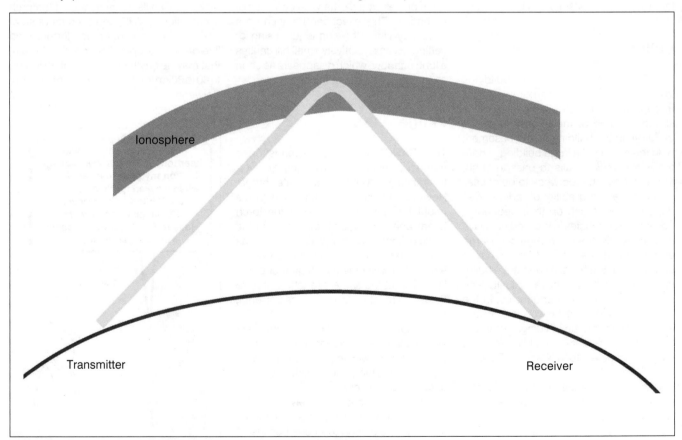

Fig 23: The ionosphere can reflect radio signals back to earth as much as 4000km away in a single 'hop'.

Licence Conditions

FROM DECEMBER 2006 the three UK amateur licences terms & conditions documents have been merged into a single document. You should check you have an up to date copy by looking on the Ofcom website.

The terms & conditions document gives all the rules you need to abide by when setting up your radio equipment and operating. For the purposes of the training and the written assessment, you are only expected to remember and understand a few of the more important issues. The other details will be of use to you during your operating and they can be read at a later date. You may find it helpful to cross out those terms in the licence that only apply to Intermediate or Full licenses.

The relevant sections of the syllabus are shown below together with the related part of the licence (in italics) followed by a few words of explanation.

1a.1 Recall that the amateur licence is for self-training in radio communications and is of a non-commercial nature.

1(1) *The Licensee shall ensure that the Radio Equipment is only used:*

(a) *for the purpose of self-training in radio communications, including conducting technical investigations; and*

(b) *as a leisure activity and not for commercial purposes of any kind.*

This simply means that you may use amateur radio to train yourself in the art of radio communication and discover how radio works. Contacting other amateurs, taking part in contests or whatever it is about amateur radio that interests you is just a part of your self-training. It also means that you should not use your radio for other purposes such as running a business.

2b.1 Recall the types of UK Amateur Licence.

Recall that more advanced classes of amateur licence exist and that they allow greater facilities and the ability to build/modify transmitting equipment.

Recall that many other countries do not currently accept the UK Foundation Licence.

There are 3 types of amateur licence. The Foundation Licence, the Intermediate Licence and the Full Licence. The privileges granted increase with the higher types of licence. The transmit power allowed increases and the number of frequency bands permitted also increases slightly. Intermediate and Full licensees are allowed to design and build their own transmitters, whilst Foundation licensees are restricted to commercially produced transmitters and commercially supplied kits. There are no international agreements for other countries to recognise the UK Foundation licence. You should not operate abroad.

2b.2 Recall the format of Foundation, Intermediate and Full callsigns. Recall that secondary identifiers are used but be able to state only those for the Foundation Licence.

The form of the callsign shows what type of licence is held.

Foundation: (eg M3ABC)

All foundation licences begin 'M3' or 'M6' and have 3 letters identifying the individual licence. In Scotland, Wales or outside the mainland, a regional secondary identifier is added between the 'M' and the number. For example, in Wales the call is MW3ABC. This applies whenever the transmission is from Wales, even if you actually live in England or the Channel Islands.

The full list of regional identifiers which you need to learn is:

D Isle of Man
I Northern Ireland
J Jersey
M Scotland
U Guernsey
W Wales

Intermediate: (eg 2E0ABC or 2E1ABC)

For the exam you need to know two things. Firstly that the current Intermediate prefix is 2E0, and secondly that the E is replaced by the regional identifier as for the Foundation Licence. So a transmission on HF from Scotland by an Intermediate licensee will be 2M0XYZ. On-air you will also hear 2E1 calls, they are also Intermediate licensees.

Full: (eg M0ABC or M1ABC)

This is all you need to know. The same regional secondary identifiers apply so an amateur transmitting from the Isle of Man will give the call in the form MD0ABC.

Historically, amateur callsigns began with the letter 'G' (eg G0HIQ), but all the letter combinations in the G0,G1,G2 etc series filled up, so the M series was started a few years ago.

In the past there was an international requirement to pass a Morse test to use the HF bands and some of the call sign prefixes were only issued to those who had.

This requirement was dropped in the UK following the World Radio Conference WRC03, allowing all amateurs access to some HF bands. Many countries have adopted this change but some do still require a Morse test.

Optionally you can add'/M' to the end of your callsign if you are mobile as a pedestrian, in a vehicle or a boat on inland water. '/A' shows you are in a building or location with a postal address that is not the address in your licence. If you are camping in a field or somewhere fixed without a postal address you may add '/P'. These suffixes are optional, but if you use them you must get them right.

2c.1 Recall the requirements for station identification.

13(1) *he Licensee, or, if this Licence is a Full Licence, then any other authorised person who uses the Radio Equipment, shall ensure that:*

(a) *the station is clearly identifiable at all times;*

(b) *the Callsign is transmitted as frequently as is practicable during transmissions, unless the specific requirements of Note (g) to the Notes to Schedule 1 of this Licence apply; and*

(c) *the Callsign is given in voice or other appropriate format consistent with the mode of operation.*

The licence requires you to make sure your transmissions can be identified to you or your station if you are supervising someone else using your callsign. It is left to your common sense to decide how often this is. For many years this was stated to be at least every 15 minutes but amateur practice has always been to give the callsign rather more frequently but not on every short 'over'.

When calling CQ it is necessary to give your callsign for two reasons. Firstly because the Licence requires your station to be 'identifiable at all times', and secondly because the person answering will want to know who you are and you will want to know they are replying to you by including your callsign in their reply.

If you are replying to a CQ call from another station, they will want to know who is calling them, and the way to do that is to include your callsign in the reply.

After a couple of 'overs' you need to give your callsign again; others hearing you may be interested and you should, just to be sure you indeed are clearly identifiable. Some stations include their callsign at the beginning and end of every 'over', but the UK Licence does not specifically require that.

If you change frequency, perhaps off a calling channel, you, and the person you are in contact with, will be new arrivals on that frequency so it makes sense to identify again. Similarly when you change the mode of transmission, FM to SSB for example, you will be 'new' to those using that mode, so giving your callsign in the new mode seems like a good thing to do. Of course if you are operating in accordance with the Band Plan it is quite likely a mode change

will also involve a small frequency change. However there are 'all mode' and digital mode sections where different modes may share the same frequency or part of a frequency band.

The reference to Note (g) to Schedule (1) is included in every Licence but is not relevant at Foundation Level as Note (g) only affects amateurs holding a Full licence.

2(2) *The Licensee shall use the following appropriate Regional Secondary Locator after the United Kingdom Callsign prefix "G", "M" or "2" as specified in Section 1, when identifying the Radio Equipment in accordance with Clause 13(1):*

(a) *England - No Regional Secondary Locator;*

(b) *Guernsey - "U";*

(c) *Isle of Man - "D";*

(d) *Jersey - "J";*

(e) *Northern Ireland - "I";*

(f) *Scotland - "M";*

(g) *Wales - "W".*

This gives the regional secondary Locator, that is the letter to add immediately after the M of your callsign if you are in another part of the UK, such as when mobile.

2c.2 and 2c.3 Recall the requirement to only send messages to other amateurs.

Recall that secret codes are not permitted.

11(2) *Unless the Radio Equipment is being used for the purposes of clauses 1(2) or 1(3) in the UK:*

(a) *Messages sent from the station shall only be addressed to other Amateurs or to the stations of those Amateurs;*

(b) *Messages sent from the station shall not be encrypted for the purposes of rendering the Message unintelligible to other radio spectrum users.*

It is worth noting that clauses 1(2) and 1(3) relate to the use of your station to help out in times of emergency, but all we need to know for the Foundation exam is that messages can only be sent to other amateurs, not their family and friends. You will probably realise on the course that you can operate under supervision and that other amateurs can talk to you.

To comply with their licence, what they

are really doing is sending their messages to the station you happen to be using. Similarly, you may talk to another trainee or a non-amateur sending what is called a 'greetings message'. These, however, are fine details that you can read up on after you have got your licence.

Many people think a code is something secret. Here it is not. The Morse code is not secret, it is simply a way of replacing words with something that can be transmitted on a very simple transmitter, so as to get the message through.

You will probably hear about 'Q codes' as an amateur. They are 3 letter codes, all beginning with 'Q'. Each have a special meaning. 'QSY', for example, means 'change frequency'. These codes are intended for use on Morse to save the time and effort of spelling out the meaning. They also have the advantage that they are international. Foreign amateurs will have a table of the same Q codes, but with their meanings written in their own language.

All the codes have, in common, the aim of making communication easier, not more difficult. Amateurs are not allowed to use secret codes or 'ciphers' as they are called except in the special circumstances in helping a User Service. An example of this might be helping the British Red Cross pass messages concerning a patient where the patient's name and circumstances cannot be disclosed on the radio because anyone could be listening.

2c.4 Recall that broadcasting is not permitted.

11(4) *The Licensee shall not send Messages (whether directly or for onwards transmission by another station) for general reception other than:*

(a) *initial calls; or*

(b) *to groups or networks ("nets") of three or more Amateurs as long as communication is first established separately with at least one Amateur in any such group;*

(c) *Messages transmitted via a mailbox or bulletin board for reception by Amateurs.*

For our purposes all we need to worry about is that amateurs are not allowed to broadcast, that is send messages to anybody who happens to be listening. There is one exception and that is a "CQ" call which is an invitation for anybody hearing to reply and make contact. Apart from CQ calls we must address our remarks to a particular station. Others will overhear the transmission and may join in if it seems polite to do so. You can address your transmissions to them as well – but not everybody.

(b) and (c) allow amateurs to formally make contact with just one person in a group rather than everybody in the group having to make separate contact with everybody else which would achieve little but waste a lot of time. You will not be asked questions on this point in the exam.

2c.5 Recall that only the licensee, or another UK licensed amateur operating under his or her supervision, may use the Radio Equipment.

Recall that in certain circumstances the licensee may allow the equipment to be used by a member of a User Service.

Note that the nature of the circumstances and the identity of the user services are not examinable.

> *3(1)*   *Subject to Clauses 1(2), 3(2) and 3(3), the Licensee shall ensure that the Radio Equipment shall only be operated by the Licensee personally and by no other persons.*
>
> *3(2)*   *The licensee may permit the operation of the Radio Equipment by a person who holds a current United Kingdom Amateur radio licence provided that any such operation of the Radio Equipment is carried out in the presence of and under the direct supervision of the licensee and that such persons are made aware of, and the requirement to comply with, the terms, conditions and limitations of this Licence.*

3(1) simply means that only you may use your equipment 3(2) goes on to say that you may supervise another UK licensed amateur using your equipment. Since you are supervising, your call sign will be used and the rules of your licence must be obeyed. That means that if you happen to be supervising a Full licensee, they will be limited to 10W transmit power. 3(3) only applies to Full licence holders. 1(2) allows you to use your radio to pass messages

for the User Services or let one of them use the radio themselves if they need to. There is always the option of a licensed visitor using the equipment as if it was their own property under their own licence and call sign. If they had a higher class of licence they could even then supervise you using the higher powers and privileges of their licence and giving their call sign in identification. This point is not examined, but you are allowed to do it.

2c.6 Recall the requirement to notify Ofcom of change of address.

> *6(2)*   *The Licensee must give immediate notice to Ofcom either in writing or by means of Ofcom's on-line licensing system of any change to the Licensee's name, Main Station Address (or mailing address if different) from that recorded in this Licence.*

If you move house then you must tell Ofcom your new address. This may be done by post or via the web-based licensing system.

2c.7 Recall that a person authorised by Ofcom has the right to inspect, require the modification, close down or restrict the operation of the Radio Equipment.

> *8(1)*   *The Licensee shall permit any person authorised by Ofcom:*
> *(a)*   *to inspect the Licence; and*
> *(b)*   *to have access to the Radio Equipment for the purposes of inspection, examination and testing; at any and all reasonable times or, when in the opinion of that person an urgent situation exists, at any time to ensure that the Radio Equipment is being used in accordance with the terms of this licence.*

Ofcom has the duty of keeping the radio spectrum clean. That means tracing sources of interference and illegal use of radio. It is possible that your radio has developed a fault of which you are unaware or that there is a problem in the locality that has nothing whatever to do with you. Either way, authorised Ofcom staff may need to check your radio. It is a condition of owning an amateur radio licence that you will let them do that.

> *5(1)*   *A person authorised by Ofcom may require the Radio Equipment, or any part thereof, to be modified or restricted in use, or temporarily or permanently closed down with immediate effect if, in the opinion of the person authorised by Ofcom:*
> *(a)*   *a breach of this Licence has occurred; and/or*
> *(b)*   *the use of the Radio Equipment is causing or contributing to Undue Interference to the authorised use of other radio equipment.*

Fairly obviously, if there is a problem with your radio then you will need to get it fixed and cannot continue transmitting until you do. The Ofcom staff would much prefer to help you operate as intended, but if you decide not to co-operate you can be ordered to close down or restrict your operation in some way.

2c.8 and 2c.9 Understand and apply the Schedule to the licence. Identify allowable frequencies and power limits.

The schedule to the licence is the table of frequency bands you can use, the status (Primary or Secondary) and the permitted powers.

The schedules for all three licences are included in the licence document and Foundation licensees use schedule A. A copy will be provided during the training course and during the exam. Even so, it is worthwhile reading it a few times so you know your way round it and understand what each item means.

A copy of the schedule and an explanation of the terms used is on page 30, but you should ensure you have the latest copy.

The questions you may be asked will be expecting you to look up the answer in the schedule. You may, for example, be asked what power is permitted in a particular band. There will be two questions, one from the HF section and one from the VHF section.

Operating Practices & Procedures

A KEY PART OF your Foundation licence training and assessment is, knowing how to operate your radio, what frequencies to use and what to do when 'on the air'. Much of this is practical and far better learned by hands-on experience, than from a book. That is the reason why the practical assessment is part of the overall examination process required to obtain an amateur licence.

Band plans

THERE ARE SEVERAL modes of modulation and types of transmitted signal in amateur radio. FM and SSB voice are common, as is CW (Morse Code). Data modes such as radio teletype (RTTY), packet, fax and slow scan television (SSTV) are all well established. PSK31 is a computer generated text mode designed to be useable even in poor or noisy conditions, is a more recent amateur invention.

These different modes do not share frequencies well, so each type of transmission is allocated a set portion of the whole band. This is all shown in the Band Plan. The allocations are made by the International Amateur Radio Union, the IARU. This is a body composed of all the national societies, the RSGB in the case of the United Kingdon, for the purpose of reaching common agreement on matters of mutual interest. Since radio waves travel world-wide, it is necessary to agree on band planning at the international level. The band plans are not licence obligations but they are a 'gentleman's agreement' on how things should be conducted. You are expected to conform to the band plans.

A copy of the band plans for the 14MHz and 144MHz bands are shown in **Fig 24**. Please note that the IARU update the band plans from time to time and the latest versions are available from the RSGB web site. During the exam, you will be provided with a copy of the band plans to use if you are asked a question on this topic, so there is no need to memorise them.

Log

It is not a licence requirement to keep a permanent Log although you can be asked to keep one by an Ofcom officer investigating a case of interference, which may or may not turn out to have anything to do with you. Nonetheless a Log is a very useful reference and will be essential if you want to send and receive QSL cards or submit entries in a competition. A QSL card is a card from your distant contact confirming the contact took place.

The Log is also useful to show when you were not operating and will often be accepted as showing the interference did not come from you. Acceptance depends on the Log being complete and up to date!

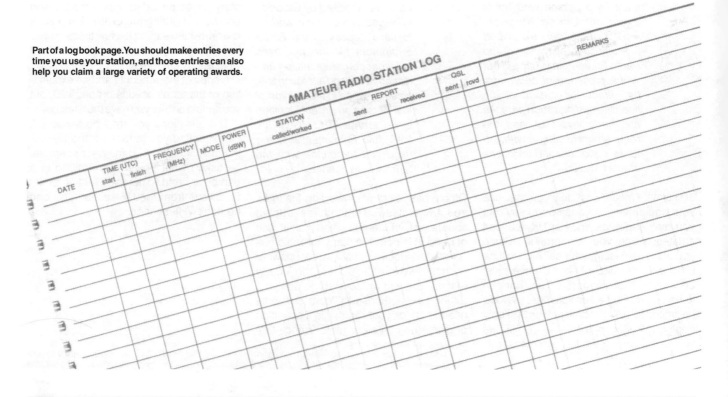

Part of a log book page. You should make entries every time you use your station, and those entries can also help you claim a large variety of operating awards.

RSGB
Foundation
Licence
Amateur Radio
Band Plans

© Radio Society of Great Britain 2007

144MHz (2m)	Necessary Bandwidth	UK Usage
144.000-144.110 MHz	500Hz	**Telegraphy and data** 144.050 MHz Telegraphy calling
144.110-144.150	500Hz	**Telegraphy and data** 144.138 MHz PSK31 centre of activity
144.150-144.180	2700Hz	**Telegraphy and data** 144.150-144.160 MHz FAI and Moonbounce (EME) activity SSB
144.180-144.360	2700Hz	**Telegraphy and SSB** 144.175 MHz Microwave talk-back 144.200 MHz Random MS SSB calling frequency 144.250 MHz GB2RS news broadcast and slow Morse 144.300 MHz SSB calling
144.360-144.399	2700Hz	**Telegraphy, MGM, SSB** 144.370 MHz MGM calling frequency
144.400-144.490		**Propagation Beacons only**
144.490-144.500		**(Guard band)**
144.500-144.794	20 kHz	**All Modes** 144.500 MHz SSTV calling 144.525 MHz ATV SSB Talk back 144.600 MHz RTTY calling 144.600 MHz RTTY working (FSK) 144.625-144.675 MHz Can be used by RAYNET 144.700 MHz FAX calling 144.750 MHz ATV Talk back 144.775-144.794 MHz Can be used by RAYNET
144.794-144.990	12 kHz	**MGM Packet radio** 144.800-144.9875 MHz Digital modes (including unattended) 144.8250 MHz Internet voice gateway 144.8375 MHz Internet voice gateway 144.8500 MHz AX25 BBS user access 144.9750 MHz High speed 25 kHz channel
144.990-145.1935	12 kHz	**FM** RV48 RV63 Repeater input exclusive (Note 2)
145.200	12 kHz	**FM** Space communications (e.g. I.S.S.) - Earth-Space
145.200-145.5935	12 kHz	**FM** V16-V48 FM simplex (Note 3) 145.2125 MHz Internet voice gateway 145.2375 MHz Internet voice gateway 145.2500 MHz Used for slow Morse 145.2875 MHz Internet voice gateway 145.3000 MHz RTTY local 145.3375 MHz Internet voice gateway 145.5000 MHz Mobile calling 145.5250 MHz Used for GB2RS news broadcast. 145.5500 MHz Used for rally/exhibition talk-in
145.5935-145.7935	12 kHz	**FM** RV48 - RV63 Repeater output (Note 2)
145.800	12 kHz	**FM** Space communications (e.g. I.S.S.) - Space-Earth
145.805-146.000	12 kHz	**All Modes - Satellite exclusive**

14MHz (20m)	Necessary Bandwidth	UK Usage
14,000-14,060 kHz	200 Hz	**Telegraph - contest preferred** 14,055 kHz QRS (slow telegraphy) Centre of Activity
14,060-14,070	200 Hz	**Telegraphy** 14,060 kHz QRP (low power) Centre of Activity
14,070-14,089	500 Hz	**Narrow band modes**
14,089-14,099	500 Hz	**Narrow band modes - automatically controlled datastations (unattended)** 14,099-14,101 IBP - reserved exclusively for beacons
14,101-14,112	2.7 kHz	**All modes - automatically controlled data stations (unattended)**
14,112-14,125	2.7 kHz	**All modes (excluding digimodes)**
14,125-14,300	2.7 kHz	**All modes SSB contest preferred segment** 14,195 +- 5 kHz Priority for Dxpeditions 14,230 kHz Image Centre of Activity. 14,285 kHz QRP Centre of Activity
14,300-14,350	2.7 kHz	**All modes** 14,300 kHz Global Emergency Centre of Activity

Note 1.
Meteor scatter operation can take place up to 26kHz higher than the reference frequency.
Note 2.
12.5kHz channels numbered RV48-RV63. RV48 input = 145.000 MHz, output = 145.600 MHz.
Note 3.
12.5kHz simplex channels numbered V16-V46. V16=145.200 MHz.

Licence Notes: Amateur Service & Amateur Satellite Service: Primary User. Beacons may be established for DF competions except within 50 km of TA 012869 (Scarborough).

Licence Notes: Amateur Service - Primary User. 14,000-14,250 kHz Amateur Satellite Service - Primary User.

Fig 24: This is a example of a simplified bandplan similar to the one you will be provided with during your exam. Bandplans exist for all amateur radio bands but only the two shown are ones on which you will be tested. Complete and up to date bandplans are available from the RSGB website www.rsgb.org/bandplans.

Transceiver controls

DURING YOUR TRAINING, you will need to use HF and VHF transceivers and become familiar with their controls.

Many VHF FM transceivers are designed for mobile use, with straightforward controls.

The main controls are:

Power on/off
May be a click position on the volume control, or a separate switch.

Tuning
Sets the transmit and receive frequency.

Volume (or AF gain)
Sets the loudspeaker volume.

Squelch (or Muting)
Silences the audio when no signal is being received. You should adjust this to just silence the background noise in the absence of a signal.

Other controls that may be present:

Repeater frequency offset
Sets different transmit and receive frequencies for use when using a repeater. This might be automatically selected when tuned to the repeater part of the band; you need to check.

A modern, portable, low power transceiver. This model covers HF and VHF bands.

Power high/low
Choice of transmit power. This may be a switch or continuously adjustable control.

Tone (or tone burst)
Selects the repeater access tone or CTCSS (see repeaters). This should be 'on' for repeater use but remember to turn it 'off' when not using a repeater.

Memory/VFO
Select main tuning dial or pre-set frequency memory.

There is also a frequency display that may also show the status of some of the other controls and an "on-air" indicator. Usually there is a received signal strength indicator.

The HF transceiver and VHF multi-mode transceivers need extra controls to select the mode of transmission and make fine adjustments to items like the receive frequency or facilities that are either not present on simple VHF FM only equipment or are factory pre-set.

In addition to the controls above, you may find:

Mode
Selects between AM, FM, USB, LSB and CW. Possibly also data.

RIT
Receiver Incremental Tuning, slightly offsets the receive frequency from the transmit frequency on the main dial and display.

RF gain
Adjusts the gain of the RF amplifier.

Microphone gain
Adjusts level of audio transmit signal. This is set to avoid overmodulation (see 'Modulation' on page 10).

Wide/narrow
Sets choice of receive bandwidth. Different modes have different bandwidth, that is the amount of radio spectrum they use. Selecting the right bandwidth allows a clean signal with minimum interference. Try changing it and listen to the effect.

Carrier level (or output power)
Varies the transmit power. Used instead of the simple high/low switch above.

VFO1/VFO2
Many 'rigs' have two VFOs allowing quick switching between them or even using '1' on receive and '2' on transmit for split frequency operation.

NB: Make sure you know which the controls are on the equipment you will be using. The controls will be very similar to those described here and your tutor will be happy to show you those on the radio you will be using.

Initial calls

BEFORE CALLING, listen on the frequency and briefly ask if it is in use. It is possible you will not hear a distant station but cause interference to a nearer one that is listening to it.

On the VHF and UHF bands there is a 'calling channel' or frequency set aside for the purpose of making 'CQ calls', which is an invitation for anybody to reply. On HF there are no set calling frequencies.

The form of a CQ call depends on whether you are on HF using single sideband (SSB) mode or on VHF using FM. When on VHF FM, the frequencies are divided up into set channels, rather like FM broadcast stations. Tuning in is easy. A call on the frequency is easily heard and replied to. On SSB, however, the tuning is much more critical and requires fine adjustment to get it right.

A VHF CQ call might be **"CQ CQ CQ this is M3ABC calling CQ"**.

Anybody hearing that will be able to reply. If nobody does, then one more call might help somebody who was not sure they caught your call sign but further calls are unlikely to have more luck. Better to wait a while before trying again.

On HF SSB, however, two things are different. Without a calling channel there is no obvious place to listen, so it is more common to tune around listening for calls. Also, when a call is heard, there is a need

A budget handheld VHF transceiver with simple controls (see inset)

to tune in accurately, which takes a little time. HF CQ calls need to be longer, to allow for the accurate tuning, and repeated a few times to allow for those just tuning round to find you.

A HF call might be "**CQ CQ CQ   CQ CQ CQ This is M3ABC, M3ABC calling CQ CQ CQ M3ABC calling CQ**".

It is quite possible that this will not be heard the first time so only a second or two need be allowed before repeating the call. It may well require many such calls before a reply is heard.

If the replying station is slightly off-tune, do not adjust your main transmit/receive frequency. The task of tuning in properly or 'netting' as it is called is down to them. It is no use both of you trying to follow each other up and down the band!

If, after your second transmission, he/she still sounds a bit off-tune, then the receiver incremental tuning or RIT control may be used to make fine adjustments to your receive frequency without altering your transmit frequency, which the distant station will, by now, have tuned in to. This does take a bit of practice to get used to the pitch of the voice and the retuning required. It seldom sounds as good as an FM contact, but good results can be achieved.

On a VHF or UHF calling channel, you should agree a working frequency or channel and then leave the calling   channel clear for others. It is bad manners to hold a conversation on the calling channel. One of you, normally the caller, will check neighbouring channels for a clear one, asking if it is use, and then advise his contact of the chosen one and agree to make contact there. Bear in mind that it is possible that he will find the frequency occupied even if you didn't. Also since you will then be on a new frequency, do not forget to give your callsign again. The minimum requirement is every 15 minutes but you should aim to give your callsign on most 'overs'.

Signal reports

IT IS NORMAL for amateurs to say how well they are receiving the other station, that is a 'signal report'. The report is based on the "RST code of Readability, Signal strength and (Morse only) Tone. Readability is on a 5 point scale from R1 - unreadable to R5 - perfectly readable and signal strength on a 9 point scale from S1 - Faint signals, barely perceptible to S9 - Extremely strong signals. It is common to use the signal strength meter which is usually calibrated

S1 to S9 and occasionally with numbers such as +10 and +20. These are even stronger signals as shown on the meter. The calibration is very approximate but useable. On FM the meter will give a steady reading but on SSB it will vary in time with the speech. You will need to give an average reading during a longer period of speech. A handy RST chart is included on the inside back cover of this book to make remembering it easier.

Many operators give a 59 signal report even when it is obviously not. It is more useful to give an honest report but bear in mind the quality of the antenna will have a considerable influence on the signal received.

An HF SSB contact

ON HF IT IS quite likely that the station replying will not be from the UK and their command of the English language rather limited. The contact becomes rather more formalised, so each party has a reasonable idea what to expect. The sequence of events might be:

CQ CQ CQ CQ CQ CQ this is M3ABC calling CQ

M3ABC this is PA1XYZ PA1XYZ

PA1XYZ Good evening, name here is Peter, location South-ampton, over.

M3ABC Good evening Peter, name Jan in Hilversum, Hilversum. Your report is 59, 59, over.

Ok Jan, your report is 5 and 7, 5 and 7, good signal.

Name, location and signal report are standard items in a contact. If communication or understanding is poor, that might be practically all that is said, especially if it is a first contact. After that it is common to exchange details of the transmitter and antenna. You may also be asked to 'QSL'. A QSL card is a postcard with the details of the contact, date time, frequency, mode and other items you may like to include. This is only likely to happen for longer distant HF SSB contacts. QSL cards are not normally sent for local VHF FM contacts.

Listen to that frequency. It sounds quiet, but I still need to ask if it is in use before I call CQ. You never know if someone we can't hear is already in contact with someone who will hear us.

Repeaters

A REPEATER IS a connected transmitter and receiver, intended to re-transmit the signal picked up by the receiver.

Clearly it cannot re-transmit the signal on the same frequency, because that would prevent the receiver from hearing anything.

Take a look at the 144 MHz band plan on page 21. The sub-band 144·990 MHz to 145·1935 MHz is shown as FM Repeater inputs, RV48 to RV63. The RV numbers are the channel numbers. They are centred on 145·000 MHz (RV48), 145·0125 MHz (RV49) and so on in 12·5kHz steps. The band starts at 144·990 MHz to allow for the bandwidth of the transmission. There are 16 channels in all. The sub-band 145·5935 MHz to 145·7935 MHz is shown as FM Repeater outputs with the same channel numbers.

The purpose or function of a repeater is to allow hand-held and mobile transceivers to obtain greater range, which may otherwise be quite limited. The repeater will be mounted on a prominent site.

So that the repeater does not re-transmit unintended noise and unwanted signals, it is fitted with one or two tone operated facilities. Historically, to 'wake up' a repeater it is necessary for the user to transmit a 1750Hz 'tone-burst' lasting about half a second. This would activate the repeater, which would then re-transmit any received signals. After about 2 minutes of non-use it would shut down and need another tone-burst. As long as it was used with only small gaps, it would stay live.

A more recent development, not yet fitted to all repeaters, is Continuous Tone Coded Signalling System (CTCSS). This relies on a low frequency sub-audio tone between 70 and 250Hz, which the user transmits all the time that he is transmitting. Different tones are used in different geographical areas, but often all the repeaters on different radio

Lots of desk microphones contain amplifiers to boost the audio, so you may need to make adjustments. This model has a slider control to do just that.

channels in the same area use the same CTCSS tone. The next nearest repeater using the same radio frequency will use a different CTCSS tone to prevent a user accidentally accessing two repeaters at the same time. These tones are filtered out before being sent to headphones or the loudspeaker.

To use a repeater, a number of things have to be done.

1. Tune to the correct channel, the output frequency of the desired repeater.

2. Select the repeater offset so that the transmitted frequency is 600kHz lower.

3. Turn on the tone burst and/or CTCSS facility, whichever the local repeater uses.

4. Push the PTT and call. It is customary, when making a CQ call through the repeater to say something like "M3ABC listening through", rather than the normal CQ call.

On some transmitters the selection of the repeater offset is shown by a minus sign in the display. The frequency readout may also change to the actual transmit frequency when transmitting.

The UHF repeaters use a +1·6MHz offset, not that you need remember that for the exam!

Desk microphones & packet TNC's

MOST MOBILE transceivers come supplied with a fist microphone. For home use

If you connect a TNC (Terminal Node Controller) between your radio and computer you will be able to send and receive text messages over the air.

a desk microphone may be preferred, leaving your hands free to operate the radio and write the log.

The output signal level may not be the same as from the supplied fist microphone. It may be necessary to make an adjustment to the output level control of the desk microphone, or, less desirable, to the transmitter input. Less desirable, because it will need adjusting again when the fist microphone is used again.

Similarly, packet Terminal Node Controllers (TNCs) often have very high outputs that need reducing considerably before feeding in to the transmitter.

A TNC is much the same as the modem used to connect a computer to the Internet, however now it is connecting the computer to the radio which will be tuned to an amateur 'packet' frequency. This is a bit like an amateur only Internet that uses text only. It does not use pictures, because of the large size (K-bytes) of them and the long time required to send them.

Sending excessively high audio levels into the microphone socket will cause distortion, unreadable signals and importantly, overmodulation which will interfere with other radio users. **It must be avoided.** Suitable arrangements must also be made to ensure the PTT is correctly wired and will successfully turn the transmitter 'on' and 'off'. It is not unknown for the transmitted RF to interfere with the TNC and result in the transmitter becoming jammed on, so be careful when setting-up.

The Phonetic Alphabet

The phonetic alphabet is used when communication is difficult, perhaps because the signal is weak or when conditions are noisy. The correct alphabet to use is shown below and in note (b) to the licence. Please use it! It is not compulsory but non-English speaking people will not recognise "A for apple" and have never heard of a place called Zanzibar. They will understand "Alpha" or "Zulu" because that is what they would have been taught

Phonetic Alphabet			
A	Alpha	N	November
B	Bravo	O	Oscar
C	Charlie	P	Papa
D	Delta	Q	Quebec
E	Echo	R	Romeo
F	Foxtrot	S	Sierra
G	Golf	T	Tango
H	Hotel	U	Uniform
I	India	V	Victor
J	Juliet	W	Whisky
K	Kilo	X	X-ray
L	Lima	Y	Yankee
M	Mike	Z	Zulu

Jargon

The use of jargon is **not** recommended in amateur radio. You should not use terms from other radio services and it is advised not to over-use amateur radio terms either. Some terms, such as Q-Codes are intended for use on Morse where abbreviations do assist communication and they can be sometimes useful when talking to non-UK stations. Listen to other contacts by experienced amateurs and vist the local club especially if they have on-air meetings. Their advice will greatly help your operating etiquete.

Etiquette

It is important to remember that anyone may be listening including short wave listeners considering becoming amateurs. Abuse and bad language are not part of amateur radio and on-air transmissions should always be polite and respectful. It is also worth remembering that radio has no boundaries and your remarks may be heard in other countries with different cultures and beliefs. Indeed it is in being able to talk with such people that gives amateur radio the richness it enjoys.

Sadly there are those who do seem to find entertainment in disrupting other people's conversations, playing music and being generally abusive. This kind of behaviour has no place in amateur radio. If you do overhear such material or feel it is directed at you, the important thing to remember is that you must not react or respond to it. That is often what the abuser wants you to do so they can send even more abuse. Talking to an unlicensed station is a breach of your own licence and could get you a bad name or reported to the authorities as well. Simply find another channel or frequency. If it is on a calling frequency or a repeater wait a while and see if the problem has ceased. The abuser should not even know he has been heard.

Advice on many aspects of operating and ethics can be found on the RSGB web site at www.rsgb.org/operating. It is worth reading!

Persistent abuse can be reported to the RSGB's Amateur Radio Observation Service (AROS) but any formal action requires good evidence, dates, times, locations and recordings and will also have to take its turn in being followed up. Obviously you must not put yourself in an awkward position but AROS operates in a strictly confidential manner with RSGB headquarters at Bedford as the only contact point.

Electromagnetic Compatibility

ELECTROMAGNETIC Compatibility (EMC) is an important topic for the radio amateur because it is one of the issues that can cause the most difficulty to the enjoyment of the hobby and the good-will of the neighbours.

EMC is the avoidance of interference between two pieces of electronic equipment.

Radio transmitters can cause interference to other radio receiving devices and electronic items that are not intended to pick up radio waves but are nonetheless upset by them.

How is interference caused?

THE TRANSMITTER is producing powerful radio signals in a home environment.

Any metalwork, wires and pipes may pick up the signals in the same way as an antenna does, and convey them into a susceptible item of equipment in a way that was not foreseen.

A hi-fi, for example, may be fine in itself and able to tolerate the radio signals. However, as **Fig 25** shows, the loudspeaker leads, the FM radio lead, leads to a separate record or mini-disc unit or even the mains lead can pick up radio signals and convey them into the hi-fi, which then suffers.

The transmitting antenna may be close to a telephone line, especially if it is overhead on a pole. The radio operators' voice might then be heard on the telephone. Possibly an electronic telephone (most are today) will be unable to recall stored numbers when the transmitter is operating.

It is also possible that the transmitter is sending unwanted RF signals back down its mains power lead, and these are then conveyed via the mains wiring into other domestic appliances. Most will probably withstand this, but some may not.

There are so many different scenarios that it is impossible to say in advance just what the effect might be.

What can be done to minimise the problem?

GOOD PRACTICE starts in the radio shack.

There is a lot that can be done to minimise the chances of problems occurring, before having to consider solutions to particular issues. Many of these precautions will also minimise the chance of the

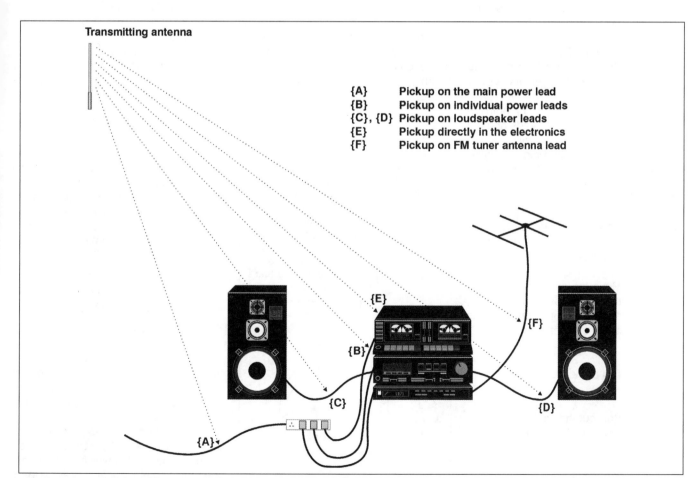

Transmitting antenna

{A}	Pickup on the main power lead
{B}	Pickup on individual power leads
{C}, {D}	Pickup on loudspeaker leads
{E}	Pickup directly in the electronics
{F}	Pickup on FM tuner antenna lead

Fig 25: There are a number of ways that a transmitted radio signal can enter a hi-fi.

amateur receivers suffering from interference from other domestic devices and making it harder to hear distant, weak stations.

First we need to be a bit more careful to consider the ways in which equipments are affected.

Direct pickup

The 'field strength' (the correct term for the strength of the radio wave) may be too high for the affected equipment. This can be more of a problem at VHF and UHF.

Cure: Reduce the field strength. Move the transmitting antenna further away, eg to the far end of the garden – so long as it is not then closer to the neighbours. It also helps if the antenna can be mounted high up, above other house wiring and TV antennas.

RF conducted from the transmitter along mains cables

RF signals may leak out of the transmitter along its power supply leads.

Cure: Prevent RF signals leaving the shack along cables by fitting suitable filters on the power leads to the transmitter. This may be necessary on both the low voltage DC leads and the mains lead. This will also assist in reducing imported interference affecting the amateur receivers.

RF from the antenna being picked up by various wires and conducted into affected devices

Cure: Move the antenna away from the house (see direct pickup, above). Fit filters on the leads into the affected device.

RF being fed back into the mains earth wires.

Cure: Sort out the earthing arrangements in the shack.

If someone tells you that you are causing interference to their television

STOP!

Resolve the problem before transmitting any more

Earthing

IN THE RADIO SHACK there are two separate reasons for earthing equipment, especially transmitters.

1. As with all equipments that are not specially made to be 'double insulated', an earth is needed for safety reasons. **This earth must not be removed.** Most amateur equipment is not double insulated.

2. Current always flows round a closed circuit or loop. Many antennas have only a single wire feed – the centre of the coaxial cable. There must be a return path for the current and this is

What kind of earth do I need on my simple station?

A one metre length of copper pipe ought to be enough. Hammer it well into the ground as close to your shack as possible. Make sure you don't try to knock it through a drain or a buried cable, and that it isn't in anyone's way.

FLNC08

normally the earth. If the transmitter earthed to the mains, then this RF sign will flow in the mains earth and via th house wiring to the other appliances the house and possibly to the neighbou as well.

RF in the mains earth can be avoidec or at least minimised, by providing an R earth in addition to the normal main safety earth. This is done by knocking metal spike in the ground close to the point where the feeders enter the house This is connected by heavy guage wir directly to the transmitter or, if fitted, the wall socket terminating the feeder to the amateur antenna.

To limit RF flowing into the mains anyway, all 3 mains leads – live, neutral and earth – need to be filtered. This is best done using a ferrite ring filter, which the mains lead is simply wrapped round. Ideally there should be about 20 turns, so it might be necessary to use 4 rings with 5 turns on each.

Choice of antenna

AT HF ANOTHER very effective option is to use a balanced antenna such as a dipole. A balun will be needed if coaxial feeder is used, and the RF on the earthed outer of the feeder is minimised if the feeder drops symmetrically away from the dipole; that is if it drops at right angles and not alongside one of the dipole halves.

End-fed HF antennas always need an effective RF earth path. Even so, the fed-end has a high current or voltage and is prone to cause EMC problems such as direct pickup and pickup by mains and telephone wiring. If an end-fed antenna cannot be avoided due to space restrictions, it is best to run the feeder down the garden and feed the antenna from the far end, ie away from the house. A good earth on the feeder braid at the feed point is important.

Power and modes of transmission

THE MORE POWER a station runs, the more likely problems are to occur. At power levels used by Foundation licensees the likelihood of problems is not high, but it is not insignificant either.

The different modes, AM, FM, SSB and data tend to cause different levels of interference. The modes which have a constant level output are far less likely to be a problem.

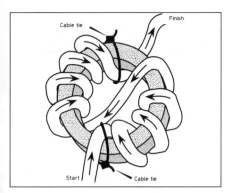

Fig 26: How to wind a ferrite ring filter.

FM

This is the most benign, since there are no level changes at all.

Single sideband

This is the worst. The level varies continuously in time with the transmitted voice and the interference caused sounds like a distorted voice which is subjectively annoying.

Data

Many of the data modes have a fairly constant transmitted power level and often cause little problem.

Morse (CW)

CW, if well keyed with smooth changes from 'on' to 'off' can be reasonable, much depending on the quality of design of the transmitter and the keying circuits.

Immunity

THE ABILITY OF equipment to withstand interference is known as 'immunity'. This quality needs to be designed in at the outset and cost is not always a good indication. The European EMC Directive now lays down standards of immunity and most modern equipment is quite good. Nonetheless, many cases of interference occur because the affected equipment is not sufficiently immune.

The immunity can often be improved by fitting suitable filters where the mains and other leads such as loudspeaker and FM aerial leads enter the device.

Ferrite ring filters (**Fig 26**) are often effec-

tive and have the considerable advantage that they do not need wires to be cut or equipment opened; both of which could have

A plug-in filter that can be used to eliminate interference from a TV or video recorder. It needs to be inserted at the antenna socket.

safety implications and invalidate warranties. Split, 'clip-on' ferrites are available (see photo below) if the plugs are moulded onto the cable.

There are other filters and a good range is available from various suppliers including the RSGB who can offer specific advice on filters in amateur radio use. The RSGB also run an EMC advisory service for members, to assist with any difficulties. The advice service is available via RSGB headquarters. The RSGB web site also has several pages of information and downloadable leaflets.

Home made filters are strongly discouraged. Their effectiveness cannot be guaranteed. Many amateurs are well qualified technically, but at the Foundation level the only good advice is to obtain ready made, tried and tested items. Fitting home made filters in mains supplies is particularly risky and special mains rated components must be used. It is not a task for the amateur who is not also professionally qualified. For the purposes of the exam as well as for your own safety, do not fit home made items in the mains.

The neighbours

THE SUBJECT OF interference is all the more important when neighbours become involved.

If neighbours have a problem with your transmissions, you have got to deal with it. It really is best if a co-operative approach can be established. Ask the neighbour if you can see what the problem is, and carry out tests to see how it can be resolved. Maintaining goodwill is essen-

A clip-on ferrite of the kind that can be used to eliminate interference.

tial if a satisfactory solution is to be found.

It is likely that you will need to stop doing whatever is causing the problem until you can solve it. Hopefully, once the problem is understood, its resolution may not be too difficult. Experience has shown, however, that often it is inadequate immunity on the part of the affected device, so you will not be able to solve the matter on your own. In such cases it is best to obtain independent assistance, but local TV repair servicemen are largely unaware of amateur EMC issues and will simply blame the amateur, often wrongly. The RSGB EMC committee (see previous) should be consulted, or a local amateur known to have expertise may be able to assist. Your local amateur radio club may also be able to suggest somebody suitably qualified.

Ofcom

IN DIFFICULT CASES it may become necessary to seek the assistance of the local Ofcom office. The neighbour can always call them and it is helpful if you can provide the address and maintain helpful contact. A joint approach is likely to result in the best solution.

The first action of Ofcom will probably be to ask each of you to keep a log of instances of interference, to narrow down the actual cause. The more information you can both give, the better.

The amateur station is likely to be inspected. This is a friendly and helpful procedure. You are not expected to be an expert, simply to have followed the advice from your training and you may be asked to keep a Log if there is an interference problem that might be caused by your transmissions. If a problem is found, then advice and help on fixing it will be available. If your station is in order, it is best if the Ofcom officer informs the neighbour. Attention can then be given to the neighbour's installation, if the neighbour requests it. There is often a fee for this service, depending on the actual circumstances.

You may well be asked to help by transmitting and, obviously, your co-operation is needed.

Safety Considerations

AMATEUR RADIO is a safe hobby, but there are always a few safety points which must be borne in mind and taken seriously.

High voltage

MAINS VOLTAGES are potentially lethal. Whilst amateurs have a habit of taking the lid off every item of equipment they own, this practice should not extend to mains powered devices. Higher powered transmitters and their power supplies may also have lethal voltages inside. Warnings on cases and in manuals must be heeded. Repairs must be left to qualified individuals.

If adjustments or replacements are needed inside equipment, they must be switched off and unplugged before work begins.

High current

HIGH CURRENT supplies also carry a risk, even if only low voltages are involved.

A short circuit can result in currents high enough to overheat wires and start a fire or cause burns. Many batteries, especially rechargeable batteries, can give surprisingly high currents which will cause wires to become red-hot.

Rings and metallic wrist watches should be removed when dealing with sources of high current.

Mains plugs & earths

THE MAINS EARTH is a safety earth, designed to protect you if a fault develops which would otherwise result in exposed metalwork becoming live. This protection also relies on the correct fuse being fitted so that the fuse will 'blow' before anything

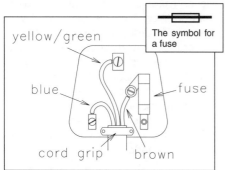

Fig 27: The correct wiring of a mains plug (a colour version of this is shown on the inside back cover of this book)

- The flex must be held captive by the cord grip. Do *not* rely on the fixing to the metal conductors themselves.
- Each wire must securely connect to the correct pin of the plug:
    Brown = live
    Blue = neutral
    Yellow/green = earth
- The insulation should continue close up to the pin.
- Frays and whiskers must be avoided.
- All the strands must be secured.
- The flex itself must be in good condition.

Fig 28: Points to remember when wiring a mains plug.

else becomes too hot. It is not acceptable just to fit a 13A fuse in every plug. A thin mains flex will overheat at well below 13A. Fit the correct value fuse and do not use higher values, even temporarily.

At the Foundation licence level it is assumed that it is inappropriate to wire mains plugs (**Fig 27**) and work inside mains powered items. However, it is still advisable to be able to recognise when a mains plug is safe (see **Fig 28**).

PME

PME or "Protective Multiple Earthing" to give its full name is a particular method of electricity supply to the home which affects the manner in which devices are earthed via the mains supply. Your electricity supplier will be able to tell you if you have a PME supply. If you have, you must consult an electrician before fitting an RF earth. The reasons are outside the scope of the syllabus but a leaflet is available on the RSGB EMC committee web site at http://www.rsgb.org/emc.

Accidents & emergencies

IN THE UNLIKELY event of an accident in the shack, there is always the possibility that the casualty may have suffered an electric shock and may still be in contact with the live mains. If another person touches the casualty then they could also receive a shock and become a casualty themselves.

The first action should always be to cut off the power.

This is best achieved if all the electrical outlets have a single 'off' switch which is clearly marked and everybody knows.

Do not touch a casualty until it is known that the power is off.

Adult help should always be summoned, and anybody who has suffered a shock should receive medical attention.

Antennas & feeders

ANTENNAS SHOULD BE mounted clear of being walked into and out of reach of being touched.

RF burns

RF burns are electric shocks from feeders and antenna elements carrying RF power. The burn may not be particularly painful, but it can be quite deep. The full extent of the injury may not be realised until some time later. Antennas must not be touched whilst transmitting, and insulated but unscreened antennas and wires can cause almost as much damage as touching the bare wire.

Powers available to the Foundation licensee are less likely to be an issue, but bear in mind that an antenna erected whilst someone is a Foundation licensee is likely to be used later, when he/she has progressed onto a higher power licence.

Antennas and their feeders must be securely mounted and well away from overhead power lines.

The wind loading on an antenna can be quite high during a gale. This may bring the antenna down, causing immediate injury or setting a trap to be walked into later. It may blow or fall against overhead power lines, resulting in all the exposed metalwork of the shack becoming live. From inside the shack, this risk may not be noticed.

If particularly high antennas are pro-

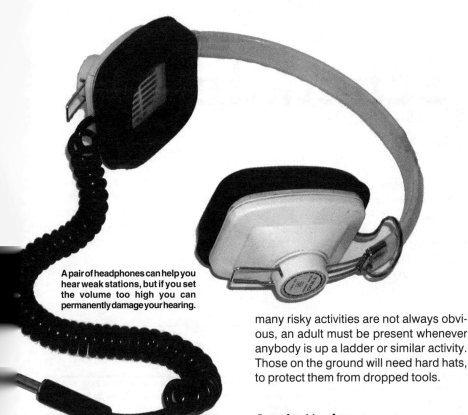

A pair of headphones can help you hear weak stations, but if you set the volume too high you can permanently damage your hearing.

later. It may blow or fall against overhead power lines, resulting in all the exposed metalwork of the shack becoming live. From inside the shack, this risk may not be noticed.

If particularly high antennas are proposed, then the risk of lightning strikes must be considered. Mast manufacturers will be able to offer advice and so will the building planning department of the local authority. There may be a need to obtain planning permission to erect large masts and advice should be sought before starting work.

Antenna erection itself is hazardous. Working at any height carries the risk of a fall, and such activities must always be supervised by a second person who is able to summon help if required. Since

> I'm pleased to see you taking sensible precautions whilst soldering.

FLNC010

many risky activities are not always obvious, an adult must be present whenever anybody is up a ladder or similar activity. Those on the ground will need hard hats, to protect them from dropped tools.

Car batteries

THE MAIN RISK from car batteries is the very high current available. However, charging them causes the battery to give off hydrogen, which can be explosive in a confined space. They should not be charged indoors, indeed using safer sealed batteries should be seriously considered. If tipped over, car batteries may leak. Their fluid contains a highly corrosive acid.

Any spills need adult attention, to be safely mopped up immediately.

Splashes

Splashes on the skin require immersion in running water for several minutes (First Aid books recommend 15 minutes).

Splashes in the eye need immediate and constant irrigation, then medical attention.

Headphones

WEARING HEADPHONES carries two risks.

Hearing

First and foremost, it is very easy to cause hearing damage.

Particularly loud noises can cause damage and pain quite quickly. For example, changing channels after listening to a very quiet station may cause momentary pain or discomfort which, if repeated too often, will lead to damage or hearing loss in the future.

More subtle, but of more concern, is simply listening too loud. It may take a year or more for this to add up to a loss of hearing, but it will be some years too late before this is discovered.

The advice is to keep turning the volume down until it is too quiet, then turn it up a little. Many take the opposite approach of turning it up until it feels almost too loud. That really is the wrong thing to do, although it may take a deliberate effort to avoid the practice.

Electrical

The other risk, when servicing equipment, is that the headphones may complete the electrical circuit and enhance the effects of an electric shock.

Do not wear headphones unless you are seated and operating your equipment normally.

Other hazards

THE SHACK may contain a number of potential hazards, apart from the risk of an electric shock. Indeed, whilst a shock is potentially life threatening, there are many other risks which could be more likely to occur.

Many tools have sharp edges, causing cuts. Soldering irons get hot and can cause quite serious burns.

Wires trailing across the floor are liable to trip people over, or drag equipment onto the floor and expose live parts.

Overhanging wires are liable to snag on people and other items.

Wires, especially mains wires running under carpets, will become frayed over time and the damage may not be noticed until it is too late and a fire or electric shock occurs.

Be careful, they'll hurt you more than you hurt them!

Licence Schedule

The schedule is a table showing the frequency bands and powers you are licensed to use. At the Foundation level you should use Table A.

Column 1

SHOWS THE FREQUENCY bands for the Foundation licence.

Column 2

SHOWS THE STATUS of the allocation to the Amateur service. There are two types of status internationally, 'Primary' and 'Secondary'. Primary status (possibly shared with other users) gives more freedom of operation. Secondary status obliges us not to interfere with users in that band who have Primary status.

Column 3

SHOWS THE STATUS of the allocation to the Amateur Satellite Service.

Column 4

GIVES THE MAXIMUM power fed to the antenna. Strictly this is measured at the point where the feeder connects to the antenna. If there is considerable loss in the feeder, eg if it is particularly long, then some increase in power at the transmitter is permitted to compensate. This assumes that the transmitter's RF power can be measured.

Notes

1. Measurement of power requires a suitable RF power meter. If necessary, the RF power can be assumed to be 2/3 of the DC power to the RF power amplifier stage of the transmitter.

Examples

1. The 7MHz band extends from 7.00 to 7.20MHz. The band has Primary status for terrestrial use, shown in column 2. For satellite use the portion from 7.00 to 7.10MHz has Primary status but the portion from 7.10 to 7.20MHz is not allocated, as shown in column 3. 7.10 to 7.20MHz can only be used for terrestrial contacts. 10W of RF power is permitted.

2. The 50MHz band extends from 50·0 to 52·0MHz. The lower part (up to 51·0MHz) has Primary status, but must not cause interference to other users outside the UK. The upper part has Secondary status and must not cause interference to other users inside or outside the UK. Again the power is limited to 10W.

Table A

Foundation Licence Parameters

Frequency Bands (in MHz)	Status of allocations in UK to the Amateur Service	Status of allocations in UK to the Amateur Satellite Service	Maximum Peak Envelope Power level in Watts (and dB relative to 1 Watt)
0.1357-0.1378	Secondary. Available on the basis of non-interference to other services inside or outside the UK.	Not allocated	1W (0 dBW) e.r.p.
1.810-1.830	Primary. Available on the basis of non-interference to other services outside the UK.	Not allocated	10W (10 dBW)
1.830-1.850	Primary	Not allocated	10W (10 dBW)
1.850-2.000	Secondary. Available on the basis of non-interference to other services inside or outside the UK.	Not allocated	10W (10 dBW)
3.500-3.800	Primary. Shared with other services	Not allocated	10W (10 dBW)
7.000-7.100	Primary	Primary	10W (10 dBW)
7.100-7.200	Primary	Not allocated	10W (10 dBW)
10.100-10.150	Secondary	Not allocated	10W (10 dBW)
14.000-14.250	Primary	Primary	10W (10 dBW)
14.250-14.350	Primary	Not allocated	10W (10 dBW)
18.068-18.168	Primary	Primary	10W (10 dBW)
21.000-21.450	Primary	Primary	10W (10 dBW)
24.890-24.990	Primary	Primary	10W (10 dBW)
28.000-29.700	Primary	Primary	10W (10 dBW)
50.00-51.00	Primary. Available on the basis of non-interference to other services outside the UK	Not allocated	10W (10 dBW)
51.00-52.00	Secondary. Available on the basis of non-interference to other services inside or outside the UK	Not allocated	10W (10 dBW)
70.00-70.50	Secondary. Available on the basis of non-interference to other services inside or outside the UK	Not allocated	10W (10 dBW)
144.0-146.0	Primary	Primary	10W (10 dBW)
430.0-431.0	Secondary	Not allocated	10W (10 dBW) e.r.p.
431.0-432.0	Secondary. Not available for use within 100km radius of Charing Cross, London (51°30'30"N, 00°07'24"W)	Not allocated	10W (10 dBW) e.r.p.
432.0-435.0	Secondary	Not allocated	10W (10 dBW)
435.0-438.0	Secondary	Secondary	10W (10 dBW)
438.0-440.0	Secondary	Not allocated	10W (10 dBW)
10000-10125	Secondary	Not allocated	1W (0 dBW)
10225-10450	Secondary	Not allocated	1W (0 dBW)
10450-10475	Secondary	Secondary	1W (0 dBW)
10475-10500	Not allocated	Secondary	1W (0 dBW)

Morse Code

HISTORICALLY, RADIO amateurs have used Morse code as it has a number of advantages, especially under difficult conditions or where people do not have a common language.

Morse used to be compulsory for access to the HF bands because amateurs share some frequencies with other radio services and Morse was often the only common mode of communication. It was therefore the only way for those services to ask the amateurs to change frequency or stop transmitting if there was a serious case of interference. That situation no longer exists, as the other services no longer use Morse code. Only a few countries now require amateurs to learn Morse code to operate below 30MHz. However, many amateurs still use Morse for their own enjoyment. The Foundation course continues to include an introduction to Morse and will show you how to continue learning if you wish to do so. For the Foundation licence there is no test as such, but a suitable standard must be reached.

The man who started it all - Samuel Morse.

During the training you will have a copy of the Morse code alphabet (see **Fig 29**), showing the letters and numbers. No punctuation or similar symbols are required.

Working with your instructor you will learn the sounds, decoding letter. You will also practice sending.

The text will be in the form of a contact between two radio amateurs,

eg   **M3ABC DE M0XYZ**
     TX HERE IS A KIT

Receiving

BETWEEN 20 and 30 characters will be sent by the tutor. You can choose the character speed and spacing in discussion with your tutor. There will be no procedural characters and the Callsigns will be M (0, 3 or 5) plus 3 letters.

You will be provided with a copy of the Morse code alphabet and may write down the dots and dashes for subsequent transcription or proceed one letter at a time.

Your tutor may re-send characters wrongly recorded, or invite you to re-check characters correctly written in Morse but wrongly transcribed.

Sending

YOU WILL BE asked to send a pre-prepared text in the same form as you had for receiving. You can make any preparations you like prior to sending, including writing the Morse code for each character to be sent and of course you will still be able to use the Morse code alphabet provided.

Your tutor will indicate which characters, if any, were incorrectly sent and you will need to re-send these correctly. This may be on a letter by letter basis, or after you have sent the text.

A	· ▬	N	▬ ·
B	▬ · · ·	O	▬ ▬ ▬
C	▬ · ▬ ·	P	· ▬ ▬ ·
D	▬ · ·	Q	▬ ▬ · ▬
E	·	R	· ▬ ·
F	· · ▬ ·	S	· · ·
G	▬ ▬ ·	T	▬
H	· · · ·	U	· · ▬
I	· ·	V	· · · ▬
J	· ▬ ▬ ▬	W	· ▬ ▬
K	▬ · ▬	X	▬ · · ▬
L	· ▬ · ·	Y	▬ · ▬ ▬
M	▬ ▬	Z	▬ ▬ · ·

1	· ▬ ▬ ▬ ▬	6	▬ · · · ·
2	· · ▬ ▬ ▬	7	▬ ▬ · · ·
3	· · · ▬ ▬	8	▬ ▬ ▬ · ·
4	· · · · ▬	9	▬ ▬ ▬ ▬ ·
5	· · · · ·	0	▬ ▬ ▬ ▬ ▬

Fig 29: The letters of the Morse code alphabet required for the Foundation Licence.

Good Luck!

The Practical Assessment

MOST TRAINING courses will include the practical assessment items at the right time during the course but it is up to you to check that all the items on your Record of Achievement have been 'signed off'. You need to have the practical work completed before you sit the examination.

Your tutor will normally arrange the exam for you as part of the course planning and the entry forms need to be at the RSGB 10 days before the date of the exam. On that day you must bring suitable evidence of identity with you, a passport or driving licence and something showing your address. If you are under 16 and do not have all the required documents, your parent or guardian may identify themselves and you, but do bring what you can.

The exam

THIS IS NOT difficult, and it is certainly not out to trick you. The number of questions on each topic is shown in the table below and a more detailed description is given in the Syllabus. There are 26 questions aimed at items which you will have covered during your course. To pass the exam you need to get at least 19 of them right.

Amateur Radio and Licensing	6 questions
Technical Basics	4 questions
Transmitters and Receivers	3 questions
Feeders and Antennas	3 questions
Propagation	2 questions
EMC	3 questions
Operating Practices and Procedures	3 questions
Safety	2 questions

The questions are 'multiple choice'. That means that there is a question and four answers, three of which are wrong and one is correct. You must show which answer is the correct one by shading in the correct box. You will have 55 minutes to answer the 26 questions, which is plenty of time.

'Do not rush, there is no need'

Example 1:

Which band of radio frequencies allows world-wide propagation?

  A The HF band

  B The VHF band

  C The UHF band

  D Both the VHF
     and UHF bands

The correct answer is A, and you should have marked that in pencil in box A for that question on the answer sheet. See "The ionosphere" and Fig 23 on page 16 if you were not sure.

You may also meet a question where the question is the first part of a sentence and the four answers each complete the sentence to form a statement. Only one of the four statements is correct, the others are wrong.

Example 2:

If an amateur changes address, he/she should notify

  A the local council

  B the RSGB (Radio Society
    of Great Britain)

  C Ofcom

  D the Police.

Answer C is correct, the other statements are wrong. If you change address you should notify Ofcom immediately on moving to your new address.

How to tackle the exam

THIS MAY BE the first exam you have ever taken. You can be forgiven if you feel a bit nervous. Different people like to do exams in different ways but some tips may help.

There is plenty of time so don't rush. Read each question carefully and all four answers. It may be simple to pick the right answer to that question, but read all the other wrong ones anyway. If you are sure, then tick the correct answer to that question in pencil on the Optical Mark Sheet which is where you show your answers. If you are not sure, mark the end of the sentence you think is correct to remind you.

When you reach the end, you will have ticked many of the questions. Now go back and read the ones you have not ticked. You may be able to see that some of the answers are wrong, so put a cross by the end of those answers. Now you have fewer answers to pick the correct one. Make your best choice, even if it is a bit of a guess. Always do that, you might be right and you

stand a better chance of being right than if you do not tick anything.

Finally, read the paper again to check you have not made any silly mistakes. If you do want to change an answer, check carefully and just use your eraser and put a pencil tick in the box of your new choice. Finally when you are sure carefully shade in the whole box in black ink but don't go outside the box. Leave time to do this. You must ink them in but you cannot then change your answer. Any marks you have made on the exam paper do not count.

All I can say now is Good Luck and remember to use all the charts and tables provided to help you answer the questions.

Applying for your licence

THE OPTICAL MARK Sheet is marked centrally and your formal result posted to you with your candidate number. Allow 10 days from the examination. If you have passed you may then log on to Ofcom licensing system using the details in your result letter and apply for your licence on-line. There is no fee for your licence but you must remember to log on at least every five years to confirm your details are unchanged, or of course, log on to change them.

Alternatively you may apply on an application form and post it to Ofcom. Unless you are 75 or over, there is a fee (currently £20) for this method of application.

Your callsign will be M6 plus three letters, and you may choose the last three letters yourself from those available. When applying for a callsign by post, it is suggested that you give a first, second and third choice, in case your preferred callsign has already been issued.

Well done! What are you going to do now?

I think I'd like to sit in with you and get a bit more operating experience, before deciding what equipment to buy.

FLNC11